THE NEW AMERICAN DREAM

Patrick Mcaulay
The New American Dream

Published by BooxAi

ISBN: 978-965-577-965-3

THE NEW AMERICAN DREAM

OR WHAT'S LEFT OF IT

PATRICK MCAULAY

CONTENTS

INTRODUCTION

What if you were one man trying to change the fate of the world for the better. How does a man go about such a thing?

"There are many problems we could address if only we put our minds together for good. Problems like pollution, trash disposal, food for all, the lack of art in the world, financial help for all and so much more that many just turn a blind eye to. They just put up with all this because they don't know anything else. Or they just plain refuse to try and change the world for the better".

1

MAKING A LIVING AND TRULY HAVING FUN

"I ALWAYS WISHED THAT I COULD MAKE A LIVING DOING NOTHING AT ALL OR AT LEAST SOMETHING THAT I LOVE. SOME WILL NEVER UNDERSTAND MY BOOK -- THOSE WHO HAVE NEVER REALLY TAKEN CHANCES IN LIFE."

This is hard to do in the times in which we live. There is hardly any time at all to enjoy the true beauties of life. I worked all summer long to acquire this damn boat of mine. I spent many hours fixing it up; it was working to create a sanctuary for me, an office, a place I could go to get away from it all.

It's a fine vessel, a 1977 25-foot carver, a beautiful boat. It is red and white with upper and lower helms, a full kitchen and a bathroom that works. Perfectly set up for life on the water with little to no care and worry about the chaos in the world around us. I know one thing: there's nothing much better than waking up in the morning on the water ... cooking breakfast, drinking coffee with a fishing pole in the water ...**the only thing better,** of course, is having a beautiful woman to accompany you while you do so. Really is nothing better than a boat goddess hanging out in damn-near no clothing. On the days spent alone, I focus on my writing. It's my way of venting about what goes on in the world.

The boat is a great way to experience nature and the wildlife. I woke up one morning to a doe on the bank getting her morning drink, taking no notice of my music blasting. I found peace in this, because the deer and I had one thing in common, we were both starting our day with no care at all but food and good drink. I decided to put the boat on Clinton Lake in Lawrence, Kansas, as rent's cheap -- only $350 a month -- a price even a bum like me can afford.

It's strange out here on this lake in the middle of America. There are tons of seagulls out here. The ocean is far from this place and they are a long way from home, but they too find a sense of security here. They just took up from the oceanside and left and managed to find a place to stay in peace. Knowing that their home was a faraway place somewhere out there in this vast country, I can relate to them because we can find home wherever we go. In the morning, nature comes to life. Everything is waking up, life starts churning again after the darkness shut it down for hours.

There's nothing better than seeing the occasional hawk flying. I don't know how hawks do it, but they circle the waters looking for their breakfast. They fly so high and they look down on the water till they find that one fish.

When they see it, they turn their boosters on and go into a sheer dive towards the depths of the lake -- faster and faster -- till they reach the water's surface, pulling up swiftly, barely scraping the surface of the water while scooping up the fish that was in their sight. It's a beautiful thing to watch: true exhilaration at sheer acrobatics. This is just a normal day in the life of a hawk. Often, I wish my days were filled with that kind of excitement: sharp turns and extreme acrobatics. Flying around catching the thermals, a day of just cruising around maintaining flight not even flapping their wings as they get in the thermals.

2

DAY TWO

Well, I left my fishing hole late in the evening. The sun was about to set on the horizon. There were red skies at night, supposedly a sailor's delight -- well, not for this sailor. Like I said, the boat is an old vessel and she doesn't have a name. So, the water gods were taking their toll; it's bad luck to have a boat without a name. Well, the boat has a name: La Osa, but some of the lettering has been removed, but you can see it through the faded paint. I think I need to paint it back to help this boat out.

I was leaving my fishing hole and the boat had been acting up. The engine was starting to lose power and surging, I thought it was a lack of fuel. I turned around and limped back to my fishing hole. I threw a few poles out in the water and began to take the carburetor apart to inspect it. While I was doing this, I had something on my line. I managed to pull in a pretty good catfish. I said, "hot damn, God has been taking care of me today." I went back to work on the carburetor and spent half the day cleaning it. When I got it all back together, I decided to see what she had in her after the work that I had done.

It was about dark at the time I left the catfish hole and with a full moon, the odds seemed to be against me. But I decided to head back

3

anyway. I took out of there and made it about 500 yards and the boat started to sputter out again. So, there I was in the middle of the lake at the mercy of nature. It's not the greatest feeling to be in a boat of this size with no power. I had a couple of paddles, but I think they would have done me better if I had just thrown them overboard. They were no use at all for this boat.

I started to diagnose the problem again and found out that my fuel pump wasn't working properly. Luckily, there was an electric fuel pump installed on the boat and I could fill the car with gas and manage to get about 3-4 minutes of run time before having to repeat the process. Well, I thought I could at least make it back to the marina like this, but like I said, the forces were against me that night.

I had almost made it back to the main channel of the lake when the boat came to an abrupt halt. "What now?" I thought. "Why was I stricken with problem after problem." At this point, I was thinking about why I even messed with this boat. I'm 26 and really have no good means for owning a boat like this. I can hardly afford to keep it afloat. At that point, I was thinking about calling an insurance company to get a policy on the thing, so I could sink it and make a profit. For about an hour or so, I thought about different ways to sink the thing. It brought great joy to me, thinking of different ways to sink it. Maybe I would just run full boar and put it straight into the rock or some trees or bring a gun out and shoot the bottom full of holes to simulate how the people on the Titanic felt.

My circumstances were a little different, though, because I wanted to sink the thing and the true terror of a boat going down would not be there. It was more fun fantasizing about the money I could possibly make watching a ship sink. I managed to get over the thought of sinking the boat and began to try and fix it once more. I tried to start the boat and it fired right up. "Weird," I thought. So, I didn't destroy the engine. I put the thing in gear and nothing. I thought that I blew the gear box right out of the thing. I got my paddles out again to see if I could possibly paddle the thing out to the main channel, but the boat didn't want to budge. I wasted about thirty minutes trying to paddle the damn thing, nearly draining all my energy with the effort. I was about to throw the paddles overboard.

I decided to jump in the lake and see if I could swim against the boat and turn it around. I never really liked the idea of jumping into the water at night, so I pondered it for about 20 minutes, wondering if the mermaids would drag me by my ankles to the bottom, never to be found again. I thought to myself. "to hell with it. If the cute mermaids take me, well, it must be my time to go," and I was almost hoping for this outcome to put an end to all this bullshit. Then I wouldn't have to worry about sinking the boat; it would be a good outcome, I thought.

I was in the middle of the lake and I thought that I was in deep water. After debating with myself about jumping into the darkened depths, I made the plunge right off the bow. Thank God I didn't dive because I jumped off into about waist deep water. That's when I realized that I had run aground. All that preparation to be swallowed by the depths of the lake and the hope of this being my last hurrah, and I landed in waist deep water. What a bummer! No mermaids or anything. That was a true disappointment.

I raised the prop on the boat, and I managed to rock the boat off the bottom and pushed it out to deeper water. Problem solved, I thought, finally back to the marina I go. I fired the boat back up and put the thing in gear. It hardly moved anywhere. I thought the gear box really was shot. Hell, I raised the prop up and put it into gear to see if the prop was spinning. It was. What the hell, I lowered the thing back and tried again. Still the same results: a slow crawl at best. But with a little hope,

I headed for the main channel once more. It kept this slow pace for about 500 yards, and I started losing steam again. I thought to myself, "I'm running at 3000 RPMs, and at this speed, I would be lucky to make it across the lake before I run out of gas. Shit, one thing after another. I almost made it out to the main channel and I lost forward propulsion completely. Still at 3000 RPMs again, I thought that I trashed my gear box. The old saying about boats was ringing in my ears about how boat stands for "break out another thousand."

After much thought about what the problem was, I decided to throw the anchor and sleep on it.

Surprisingly, I slept very well even though I was a sitting duck with no means of flying away. After a good night's sleep, I awoke and thought "Here we go again." I started the boat up, hoping that the damn thing somehow fixed itself as I slept, but with no luck. I did, however, find out that I had spun my prop in the mud the night before, but the gearbox was in good shape. "Thank God," I thought. I remembered that I had a spare prop and looked under the floorboards for it. I kept a lot of spare parts under there just in case I had minor issues, which is a must when operating an old boat like this.

The prop wasn't in there though I had taken it out a few days prior to see about having it fixed because the blades were broken off. But it did have enough blades to move the boat at a snail's pace and possibly make it back to the marina. If only the damn thing was in the boat, I would be on my way. The wind that morning was sort of in my favor blowing towards the main channel and towards the (missing word). So, I pulled the anchor and got the paddles out, to see where the wind might drift my boat. At last, I had a little bit of hope. I drifted a little way and tried to paddle, but the boat sat high out of the water and it caught a lot of wind. The paddles were, again, no help at all.

I continued drifting and made it to the barrier that surrounds the swim beach at the lake. I was drifting right towards the "No Boat" buoys. I was forced to throw my anchor again, but at least I was in a good spot, close to land and close to a road where I could possibly flag somebody down.

It was a foggy morning on the lake, at times maybe only one hundred yards of visibility at most. I could see a few boats out on the lake. It was the early morning fishermen testing their luck. They were all far out and I tried to get one of their attention, but the horn on this thing sounded like a dying cat, a god-awful sound no louder than a faint whistle no use in these conditions. I did have a spotlight and I thought that maybe I could signal someone in with it and possibly catch a ride back to the marina to retrieve my prop, but again no luck at all signaling anyone. At least I had a kitchen on the boat, so I put some coffee on and started to cook some breakfast eggs with red peppers, quite a nice breakfast but still with no avail of flagging down another boat. I was drinking my coffee and remembered that I had some bottle rockets on board for special occasions, nothing better than fireworks to bring out the inner child in you than shooting off a few fire crackers. I thought that maybe I could get a boat's attention with them. So, I grabbed a handful of bottle rockets and my coffee and climbed to the top of my boat and started to launch a few out into the lake. I would light one and wave my arms frantically at the nearest boat to me. They were all about a half mile out, I would guess, but really it just turned into me smoking cigarettes and shooting bottle rockets off the boat while enjoying my coffee. Man, did this bring a smile to my face even though I was still stuck out on the water, but at that point, I really didn't care anymore; I was just a kid shooting bottle rockets. Around that time, I think the closest boat thought that I was shooting at them or something because after about a dozen of them, he took out of there like a shot from a gun. I really don't know, though, but I hoped that maybe he was heading to get me some help, but I didn't have my hopes up.

The fog was beginning to clear finally, and I sat down to eat my breakfast, waiting for the marina to open so I could call them to see about a tow. They opened at eight am. So, I waited till then to give them a call. It was eight fifteen when I made my first call to them and no answer. "WHAT THE HELL" I thought that it would be my luck that no one showed up to work today, so I called again and still no luck. I sat back a minute, then I decided to call Clinton state park and they didn't answer either. At this point, I thought that I was the only person awake around here. Maybe the world stopped, and no one was going to work today, maybe a great catastrophe happened and I would never know because I was out here on this broken-down boat, but I kept a good head on my shoulders. The coffee was good, and the eggs were excellent, and I shot some fireworks off, it was a good day so far, I thought. It takes a lot to ruin my fun anymore, I'm used to problems at this point in my life. I always must figure something out or work on something it comes with the territory of my life I guess, but that's just part of the game; I just keep my head up and keep on keeping on its the only option these days.

It was time to call the marina one more time, the phone started ringing in my ear, riiiinnngg as I waited to hope for a reply on the other end, riiiinngg its about eight forty-five at this point, riiinnggg I crossed my fingers for luck finally a reply. They picked up the phone, they must have had a rough night of drinking, I thought, since they showed up forty-five minutes late for work. A lady with a sweet soft voice answered the phone; the sound of her voice gave me great relief, at last a response. I couldn't imagine being out on the ocean waiting for a response, like minutes would turn to hours, it would not be fun at all. After talking to her and explaining my situation, she informed me that the marinas insurance policy would not allow them to tow any boats with their rentals and that there wasn't anything that she could do. She did give me some leads, however, of some people that I could call for help and she told me to enjoy my coffee and laughed at the fact that I was in such a joyful mood for the situation that I was in. I told her to offer any person with a boat one hundred to two hundred dollars cash to come out and help, she said that she would and that she would call me if anyone took the bait. I thanked her, and she hung up the phone. The lady gave me three numbers, one was a man that she said used to tow boats but didn't know if he did anymore. I gave the man a call and he told me that he was out of business and I asked the man if he had any leads and he had no one in mind. "WELL, SHIT" I thought the second number was the parks department that I had tried to call previously. I made the call to them again with disappointment; the lady informed me that they had no tow service and she gave me the number of the sheriff who was the last person on the list as well as the last person I wanted to call since I had a few Kansas warrants out for me only for petty offenses but none the less they were warrants. I was running out of options though I just hoped the swine wouldn't show up and just haul me away back to Kansas City. I called anyway with good faith, I had to call dispatch, they asked for my name and I thought I was fucked right there.

They had me right where they wanted me if they wanted to pick me up, no chance at all. I was just a sitting duck in the middle of the lake and the worst part was I had to call them. So, if they were to arrest me, I called them to haul me in. Dispatch informed me that they were sending an officer out to help. They said they had a boat at the marina and would send it out for a tow, so I hung up the phone and the waiting game began. I figured they were going to run my name and check my background to dig up my past. Most likely, guns a blazing when they showed up. The whole time I was curious if I had just turned myself into the damn authorities. "SHIT" I thought, here comes the damn hand cuffs, god do I hate the cuffs, they always slap them on so tight, but with my experience, I have learned to be nice and respectful to the swine and if you're lucky you can ask them to loosen them for you, so they don't cut into your wrists. Cops really aren't so bad just the key to dealing with them is to treat them like people because that's what they are they are just people like you and me, if you give them respect, they will give you respect in return. Just like anyone with a kind head on their shoulders. But if you're an ass hole, you better expect to get roughed up a little bit and the cuffs will be tight, I have learned to avoid these kinds of confrontations. So here I was calling them to haul me in or at least that's what I thought.

I waited for the sheriff to show up and he called me, telling me that the boat belonged to the park rangers and he did not have access to it. I told him that would be ok because I had a prop in my car and if he could give me a ride to the marina so that I could fix my boat. About fifteen minutes later, he pulled into the swim beach parking lot and I had to swim to shore. Luckily, I could swim to the barrier and grab a hold to keep afloat because it was quite the trip to land. When I got to shore, he said to hop in and that he would give me a ride to the marina so that I could get my prop out of my car. He told me that I had to ride in the back so that I wouldn't get his car wet. I felt as I was climbing in his car that the trip to jail was beginning they finally got me. I was in nothing but a swimsuit and I was thinking to myself, at least when they book me, I won't have a lot of belongings on me to check into jail, not even a shirt on my back.

I called myself in and now I'm trapped in the car with no return anymore. He called in on his radio and I was thinking that he was calling in to inform them that they had me and were bringing me in, but he said that he was taking me to the marina. I had a sense of relief at that point, knowing that we were just headed to my car. We had a good talk, he was a good chap, a younger sheriff. I told him what I was thinking about this country today and how we all get taxed too much and are losing more and more freedoms every day and to my surprise, he agreed with me that the times were changing.

We got to my 53 Buick in the parking lot of the marina and I told him that's my car; he looked at it after seeing my boat and asked what I do for a living. It seemed like he was more curious about what sort of drugs I sold and who I killed to get this stuff because not many twenty-six year old's have these kinds of things and I told him that I fix and restore things and that I had left my party days behind which was semi-true, and that I mostly just save money now. He listened to me, but he still had a hint of suspicion about me, but he didn't ask anymore. He got out and looked at the car, admiring my work. I grabbed the prop from the back seat and we both hopped back in the cruiser. I had the prop with me in the back seat, so I didn't think that the cop took me as a threat anymore. If he did, he sure as hell wouldn't let a mad man in the back of his car with a jagged old boat prop, a perfect weapon if used as one. He began talking about technology and how it's robbing the children of their childhood, we both agreed the world was heading in a bad direction. I asked him if he had seen the movie idiocrasy and he said he had. I told him, now that movie is spot on with how the world is going today, it's scary. He agreed again, we concluded that everyone was being dumbed down and their drive for life and freedom was slowly going away. We both laughed about it as we pulled back into the beach parking lot. It was probably the most pleasant ride I had ever had with a cop and the cool thing was that we both kind of saw things from the same point of view. Not very often the cops and the outlaws get along like this.

That's why the cops aren't so bad because they came and helped me out of a tight spot that only the police would help me out of. I'm sure too, that he ran my name before he showed up and I guarantee he knew that I had warrants, but he put that all aside because I needed help. So, I appreciate the police for having people's backs.

Now I had the task of swimming back to the boat with the prop tied to the strings of my swim trunks. If you have ever tried to swim with an anchor tied to your waist, you might understand where I'm coming from and that it is no easy task. The sheriff asked me if I had a life jacket and he asked if I was going to be alright for the swim. I told him that I should be fine. He told me that he would sit on shore to make sure that I made it, but the fact of the matter was that I was so far out, even if I was to start drowning, there would have been no way for him to reach me in time. I got to the end of the swim barrier and no longer had anything to float with I had about one hundred feet to the boat and the fight started. I made it about halfway and started to get worried about what I got myself into. I felt like I was in navy seal training and the bastards were trying to drown me, but I maintained my composure and breathing, and barely made it back to the boat. I climbed back on the boat and gave a wave back to the sheriff to let him know that everything was ok. He went back to his car and drove away. I had a moment of relief as he drove away because he didn't bust me. I think he just saw a kid trying to make the best of life after being through the ringer and back.

The old beat-up prop went back on with ease and I was on my way back to the marina at a slow pace but was keeping steam. I half way expected the sheriff to be waiting for me at the marina, just being nice enough to let me get my boat back safe before taking me to jail. I looked in the parking lot for his cruiser as I approached, and it was nowhere to be in sight. The day had just got a lot better, after all I didn't sink the thing and it was back safe and sound. When I got back to my slip, the boat looked like hell a complete disaster had gone on onboard. The whole thing was covered in mud from getting in and out and pushing the boat also from pulling the muddy anchor on and off the bottom, getting mud all over the bow. It was a great mess with a broken prop to tie it all together. The prop was an easy thing to get together, but it cost me 250 dollars, a pretty penny for a kid trying to live on a budget. I could not stand to look at the boat in this condition and think about how I was going to clean the thing. It's going to take a full day to clean this mess up, but I got to work on it and it only took a few hours. I had to go back to Kansas City to buy the new prop and I had to wait a few days for it to come in, but luckily, I had a few days of work lined up it the city. I at least made money to replace the prop and managed to scrape up a couple of hundred extra dollars to live on for the rest of the week. It had been three days and I was getting worried about the boat hoping that I didn't damage anything after running it aground. I halfway expected the damn thing to be sunk when I came back. I picked up the prop and headed back to the office or at least that's what I called the boat. I have done quite a bit of work on the thing, making improvements because I have been wanting to try and sell the thing to turn a profit.

The way that I acquired the boat is a story on its own. I saw the thing on the internet and I wanted to go look at it, they wanted thirty-five hundred for it. I only had about a thousand dollars in my pocket and I went to look at the thing. Really, I was interested in looking at the design of a boat of this size, never really spending much time around boats. Buying it was just kind of false hope because I only had the thousand. I started looking at the thing and it had been sitting out of the water for quite some time and the outside had mold and moss growing on it and it looked rather rough. The woodwork around the windows needed to be completely redone as well as it was very weathered. I offered the man the thousand dollars and he said he couldn't sell it for that price, really, I had around two grands but was only willing to spend the thousand; I might have budged to fifteen hundred, but I stood my ground not really needing a boat. Luckily the man had a bunch of old cars on his property, so we got to shooting the shit and walking around as we talked about his different cars. I told him about my 53 Buick and he took me to a different shop where he had some of his older cars. The whole time he was showing me around,

I kept trying to talk him down on the boat, but he wouldn't budge at all. We started walking back to my motorcycle, so I could leave. I started asking him if we could do a trade for work or work out some sort of deal, making my final effort of getting the boat. He then asked what I could do, and I told him the long list of things that I had done in life. We couldn't find any services that he needed to be done, then I told him that I had done some tree work and that was the key to getting the boat.

Now we were getting somewhere, we walked around the house looking at the different trees that he needed to be trimmed and the price started adding up to about the price of the boat; he wanted me to do the work and still pay the thousand. I lucked out when he brought his wife out and asked her if there were any more trees she wanted to be done and she added a few more; it was about three removals around the house and trimming two large oaks and a smaller hickory over the house and barn. We got to talking price and it was about to add up to them paying me, but when the man's wife asked what the deal was, her husband said, "the work and he pays a thousand dollars for the boat," and his wife smiled at me and said we will just make an even trade for it. I got excited, but you could tell that her husband wasn't very pleased with the deal, but we agreed.

It took me a week of ass-kicking work to finish. I also had to drive an hour trip every morning to get there, but they let me stay a few nights so that I could get an early start. They offered to let me sleep in the house, but I told them that I would rather just sleep in the boat. The man's wife thought that it was kind of funny for me to sleep in the boat when they had a perfectly good room in the house. I enjoyed those nights on the boat, pretending that I was on the lake, knowing that in only a few days the boat would be mine. I even got lucky because the man and his wife helped me do some of the work and his wife even made me lunch during the day; they were some of the best people that I have ever met. I got to use the old man's tractor the last two days to haul a tree to the back of their property, where I got to have a massive bonfire that I kept feeding for two days to get rid of the debris. All the work panned out nicely, nothing like the trade and barter system. It's a good system if you can get it to work for you, but it's kind of hard to come by these days.

It was mid-September by the time I got the boat to the lake. Lots of work needed to be done, including an engine rebuild on my van that I needed to do just so I could pull the damn thing. It took a couple of months to get to enjoy it. The weather gets cool in mid-September, so I needed a heater for the nights, but the nights were the best time to be on the lake, far away from the lights of the city you can see all the stars. Some nights I could get lost in the vast number of stars in the sky. I could almost sit back and travel through space and time watching them. Seeing the occasional shooting star zip across the sky. There's a sense of relaxation while looking at the stars, a sense of limitless possibilities the world has to offer. I often sit under the stars and think about things, like past loves, possible future loves, and getting a second chance with the one that got away. There's always one love that I think about and she never seems to escape my mind. She was perfect; hell, she is perfect, in my opinion. I always dreamed of the day she would let me take her out on a real date and cruise through the night, maybe to end up on the boat to sit and reminisce on the years that had gone by since the last time we got to see each other. I think everyone has a love like this; the one that got away. It's a hard reality, but shit happens and you just must find a way to move on, I guess. Life can get lonely out by yourself but luckily at the lake there are animals to help keep you company, they are the best part of the lake life. A primitive sense of freedom, after a few days away from all the hustle and bustle, a true sense of freedom. I had a sense that my luck was about to change. Things can only get so bad before your luck has to turn around.

3

AN AMERICAN TRIP

It was sometime in June, I decided to try and take the old 53 Buick on a short American road trip. I had bought the car the previous winter for two thousand dollars. It is a superior driving machine for its age. It's all original, engine and all. The interior is ratted and torn, as you would expect from a car that is almost seventy years old. Most people would have laughed at the proposition of driving something that old on a long trip like this, but I never turn down a chance for an adventure and a good story opportunity. I didn't know what was going to happen. But I grabbed the keys and went

My destination was Tahlequah, Oklahoma, it was a place my family had visited for years. We went there on an annual float trip to float the Illinois River. It's about a five-hour drive from south Kansas City, with the last hour or so through a hilly region of Oklahoma. It's a nice peaceful drive right at the end of the trip. It sounded like a piece of cake. I had to gather supplies before I left town, first off for a trip like this, I needed beer and plenty of it. I also swung by my local cigar shop and picked up a half dozen cigars for smoking on the river. I had a hint of hesitation on whether this was a good idea. "Fuck it" I thought if the damn thing breaks down, I might have to just abandon ship and hitch hike the rest of the way.

I grabbed some Jack in the Box and ate my food in the parking lotwith an uneasy feeling in my gut. I called my dad to let him know that I would be on my way and to expect me late in the night. I finished my burger and cracked a beer and hit the road. When I hit the highway, I kept her right at about 85, which is a rather fast speed considering the age of the car, but it handled it beautifully. Windows down and wing windows cracked, beer in one hand and a cigarette in the other. The true American road trip, pure adrenaline and excitement!! Finally, I relaxed making way, sailing at a good speed and passing traffic as if it was standing still. I had made it about an hour out of town and a couple of beers down when I kept smelling something burning. I kept putting it off as if it was just a car in front of me I was smelling, but me being the adventure-seeking mad man that I am, I just kept barreling down the road.

I got about another thirty miles down the road and I started to smell it even stronger at this point. Still just ignoring the smell and making way. It was starting to get dark and I had just got out of the south end of Pittsburg, Kansas. I was in-between Pittsburg and the next town to the south. It was dark now and I had to turn my headlights on. Everything seemed to be ok, even the burning smell had gone away, "GOOD DEAL" I thought.

Now I forgot to mention the real reason I decided to drive the old car down there in the first place. My son was supposed to be there, and I hadn't seen him in years. I was only fourteen when he was conceived. Not nearly old enough to even consider raising a child. I'm known as his uncle. My real uncle ended up adopting the boy and his name is Damion. I really wanted to show him what his dad did for a living, even if he didn't know I was his dad, at least I would be the cool uncle driving a cool old car. I wanted to show him something that he could remember me by. So, I gave it a whirl to get the thing down there, so he could see it. I had just painted the whole thing, so it looked very sharp. I was proud of the work that I had done, and I wanted him to see it.

It was now pitch black and I noticed that the headlights were starting to go dim, "WEIRD" I thought, but I just kept driving. The more miles I drove, the worse the headlights got. At this point, they were so dim I could hardly see anymore. Suddenly, I realized I had a problem when the lights cut out and the engine began to stutter. At this point, I knew I had a major problem. It was an electrical problem and the car was running on battery power alone. I turned off the lights and drove in the dark to conserve power to hopefully make it to the next town. I was about to town when I saw a porn shop, a perfect place to stop at. It was the only place around with the lights on, so I decided to stop and ask for help. I walked in and there was an old man working the counter. It was probably about ten o'clock at night and I was surprised that the place was open. I was glad that it was, I told the man that I had a 53Buick that I was road-tripping and the man's face lit up. I told him I had a charging issue and needed a jump or a battery charger. The man was more than willing to help. It's nice when you meet good people along the way. He grabbed his charger and an ohm meter to help diagnose the problem. We popped the hood and looked inside; the wiring harness to the voltage regulator was fried. We charged the battery and the car fired back up and I took a reading with the ohm meter and everything seemed to be working. We had thought that we had fixed the problem.

I thanked the man and shook his hand. I got back in the car and hit the road. I got about ten minutes down the road and the same problem occurred. Luckily, I was pulling into town. I had to turn the lights out again to limp it the rest of the way into town. I made it to the local gas station, so I pulled in and parked. I popped the hood again to try to fix the car again. Since the hood was popped, some of the locals stopped to talk about the car and asked what was wrong with it. A few different people put in their two senses and tried to help. I traced the wires to see if I could find a short somewhere. I went through all the wires and couldn't find anything obviously wrong, except the casings on the wires were burnt away from the short. I spread all the wires apart to keep them from touching each other and tried the car again with no success.

I took a break and walked into the gas station to ask if it was ok for me to stay in the parking lot overnight. They told me that it was ok, so I got some pizza and went back outside to try some more. I was checking fuses and anything I could possibly think of. A man and his girlfriend pulled up next to me and I asked them if they had a screw driver to remove the light switch so that I could check it. I had some of my own tools with me but did not have a damn screw driver for some reason. The man was happy to loan me one and he started looking under the hood to see if he could possibly spot the problem but to no avail. He went inside, and I continued to look around and used the tool while I had the chance. He came back outside, and I thanked him for the help and we went along on his way.

About that time, the police showed up. As they pulled in, I was a little worried about the fact that I had a warrant in Kansas. I half way thought that they would run my ID and quickly arrest me, but to my surprise, they just asked me if they could help with anything. They did tell me that they had a jumper box to jump people's cars. I told them my story and that I was just trying to get to Oklahoma. I told him that parts for the old Buick were getting hard to come by and that I didn't know if I could fix it or not. To my surprise, he told me that he had a friend in town who had an old scrap yard full of old cars and if I was lucky, the man might have the part that I needed. It was about eleven o'clock at this point, so I had no hopes that his friend would answer, but the man did. The officer told me that his friend was on his way to look. With a bit of relief, I sat back and relaxed a while till he showed up. When he got there, he came with a posse. The group had been drinking somewhere, but they didn't seem to worry about the cops. The cops did call them to come and help so what could they do. I myself was lucky that the cops didn't investigate the floorboards of my car, otherwise they would have seen a mountain of empty beer bottles stuffed on the floor.

The man told me that he would go and check the yard to see if he had another voltage regulator that would work for my car. He went back to his yard to check. I sat waiting for quite some time, bullshitting with the police. This must be a quiet town if the cops just hang out at the gas station all night. "FINALLY," the man from the yard called. He said that he couldn't find one. All he had was one off a Pontiac Star Chief and that it would not work. I think it might have, though because Buick and Pontiac were both owned by general motors and parts back then were generic between the different makes. I was pretty sure that it would have worked, but whatever I had to come up with a different plan. I again sat back and pondered on the situation. I could not figure out a different plan. I told the cops that the gas station told me that it was ok to stay in their parking lot that night. About the time I was planning on going to sleep, a man and his wife pulled into a gas pump driving a golden Buick. The old man saw the car with the hood popped and came right over, telling me that he really liked the car and that his family used to have one when he was a kid. We began to talk, and the man asked me what was wrong with it, so I told him that it had stopped charging. He told me about an old farmer trick they used on their old tractors and cars to convert them into a modern-day alternator. He said it was very easy to do. You just had to mount a single terminal alternator to the existing brackets from the generator. Just run the single wire from the new alternator to the battery, he said. I shook the man's hand and thanked him for his help. I asked the man if I could get a jump so that I could get to the auto parts store. The police were still there, though, and they heard me ask and said that they would use their jumper, I accepted their offer. We sat and bullshitted some more while the battery was charging. He said that he was glad that I found a solution to my problem. After about thirty minutes, the car fired right back up and purred like a kitten.

The auto store wasn't very far, but I limped there just fine. I pulled into the parking lot with great relief lifted from my shoulders; at last, I could get some rest. At that point, I grabbed a beer and lit up one of my cigars to celebrate. It was one or two in the morning at this point. I was enjoying my beer and smoke when an old man driving a golf cart showed up out of nowhere. The man was eighty or ninety years old and there was something a little peculiar about him. It was almost as if the man was a ghost. When he spoke, it seemed as if he was sleep talking and wasn't there. He told me that he had a problem sleeping at night and he liked to take his golf cart out and watch the traffic go by. Who knows how many years he had been doing this, but he seemed washed up and worn out. We had a few conversations about the past and talked about the old car and some of the cars that the man used to have. He told me that I could come by his house if I needed to make a bracket to mount the new alternator and that I could use his shop. He also knew what time the truck showed up in the morning and told me if I was lucky, maybe they would open early for me. We said our goodbyes and he drove away into the darkness. It was an interesting ordeal, but he was a good old man.

I finally managed to get a few hours of sleep. When I woke up, the store had been open for about an hour. I was kind of curious what the people working thought about me sleeping in the car. They didn't say anything, but they did have the alternator and the wire that I needed as well as enough tools to fix the car. The belt pulleys didn't quite line up and the alternator was only bolted in with one bolt. I could not get the belt to tighten very much, but it was enough. I had to ask for another jump to try and crank the car over. The Buick had a starting feature in the pedal, so you had to turn the key on and push the pedal down to start it, but I found out the wires to the switch were fried as well and it no longer worked. Luckily, I had worked on the starter before and I knew how to bypass the pedal start. It required me to crawl under the car and jump across the cylinoid posts. First try it didn't start, but I got in and pumped the gas and got back underneath and the thing fired right back up. Back in business. I hopped in the cab and checked the gauges to see if the car was charging again and it was. I put her in gear and hit the road.

I was only about a quarter of the way there, now most people would have turned around and gone home, but I was on a mission to show my son the car, so on my way I went. I kept an eye on my gauges to make sure that everything was ok and kept going. It was a new day, so I cracked another beer and lit up a smoke to relax. The jimmy-rigged alternator system worked well on the slower highways, but when I hit the freeway, I ran into more problems. When I would accelerate to pass cars, the belt on the alternator would slip, since it was just tightened with one bolt. The belt was not quite tight enough. It caused the pully to smoke the belt and smoke would billow out from under the dash. At that point, I was worried about the belt snapping. I decided to stop at the next auto store to buy an extra belt and they are easier to find a new one before the old one snaps. I piled into the auto store and had them check my battery with a volt meter, everything checked out. Now I had a new belt and no worries about making it now. Even if I did burn a belt up, I had a new one to replace it.

Finally making way again, I had made it about half way and it was all interstate, so back to cruising eighty miles per hour cruising, passing cars like they were going out of style. I was finally relaxed again and had fate in the old car once more; it was a good feeling when the car was running like a top. It was like a time machine. I swear if I focused very strongly, the traffic around me would turn into cars from the forties and fifties. It was if time was standing still and I was the only one moving forward. I always wondered if people could see what I saw because it was a very cool experience to be able to travel in time. Maybe it was just a figment of my imagination, but it's as real as day to me. It's like the music starts playing and I can fly anywhere in the world or any time period I want. After zoning out for about one hundred miles, I was getting close.

I got off the interstate to fill up with gas and get some cigarettes. When I came out of the store, there was an old man looking at the car. I told him about my trip in the car and he was thoroughly impressed that I would even try the trip, especially solo. His daughter then got out of the car and she asked if she could take a picture of the car, I said that would be fine. That always the best thing about driving an old car is how the children see it. I really enjoy how it brings smiles to people's faces. That's why I like to drive it everywhere that I go. Once, I was driving next to an elderly couple. The man was driving and his wife was in the passenger seat and the old woman looked completely out of it. She had her head against the window, I would guess she was around ninety years old. As I pulled up next to them at the light, the woman perked up with excitement. I don't think the woman could speak, but she was pointing and smiling at the car with excitement, it made my day. Just the sight of the old car sparked something in her and it brought her out of her funk, even if it was just temporary, she went from a zombie-like state to full of energy and life. Just by the sight of the car, sometimes I feel that driving the car around is doing the community a favor. I hate to see the old cars cooped up in garages because they bring great joy when you take them out for a spin.

It was now the final leg of my journey. This part was all backroads with lots of curves and great views of cliffs and the river I was going to float the next day. It was a very scenic leg of the journey until I had to climb a few steep hills and the cab of the car would damn near be filled with smoke by the time I crested the top of the hills. The load of the engine pulling the large car up the hills was just smoking the belt away at great speeds. Let's put it this way I didn't need to smoke cigarettes because the car was smoking me out just fine. After a while, I got through the hills and pulled into Tahlequah. "THANK GOD" I thought, finally in town. I stopped to pick up beer for tomorrow and some more smokes for good measure, leaving the car running so that I wouldn't have to crawl under it again to start it back up. There were only five miles left till I made it to camp. I pulled in with a smile on my face knowing that I had beat the challenge and made the trip. My dad and family looked at me in shock that I had kept my hopes up and I kept going. It was a true test of the wits and I came out on top because of my experience in my past. It paid off in the long run, so my work proved successful. All there was to do was enjoy myself and wait for my boy to show up the next day.

It was one o'clock when I arrived at camp, so I had the rest of the day to enjoy myself. I drank a few beers and I took a walk down to the river's edge. The water was clear and the temperature perfect for the hot summer's day. I sat at the river's edge, drinking my beer and cooling off. I was wearing a straw hat and shades. As I sat there, I noticed a beautiful girl sitting on the bank a way down the river. She had an elegance about her, she was blonde and wearing a red swimsuit. I sat and watched her as she swam through my dark shades, hoping she wouldn't notice me watching. There was a great sense of peace that I felt watching her walk slowly into the water. She walked way out till the water reached the back strap of her swimsuit, then she just went for it and dunked herself in. She came up from the river looking like an angel that had been blessed by the river as she flipped her hair back. She was now soaking wet as she walked back to shore and the sun was glistening off her tan skin and she laid down to soak up the sun. I sat wishing that she would walk up the beach towards me, I think I would have suffered a major heart attack if that was the case just from her sheer beauty, she was pure bliss. I finished my beer and walked back to camp. When I sat down, I noticed the girl walking up the road to her campsite that just so happened to be right across the road from my campsite. I would guess that she was around twenty; she must be a good girl though, because she was there with her mother and father. I thought to myself how it would be nice to find a girl like that, family-oriented and extremely beautiful.

It was getting dark and my family was starting the fire to cook dinner for everyone. They got it going fast and we all sat around to talk about life and catch up with everyone. It had been a year since we had all gotten together, we shared stories with each other till about eleven. Now it was time to kick back and drink beers and really start to enjoy myself. It was a good feeling to sit back and watch the fire with the reflection gleaming on the side of the car. It was a glorious sight to see and a great sense of relief and accomplishment.

4

FLOATING DOWN THE RIVER

I didn't bring a tent to sleep in but luckily, the Buick has a rather large front seat and I knew it wasn't too bad to sleep in from the night before at the parts store. The next morning, I woke up early in the morning. I walked strait down to the river, grabbing a morning beer since I was on vacation. Normally I wouldn't start the morning in this way, but when I don't have shit to do, I prefer to start the morning off with a strong drink, it helps to ready myself for the day on the river ahead. There's something satisfying about it. I sat on the bank of the river to collect my thoughts. I also found out that morning that my uncle was not going to make it because there was a chance of bad weather, but I really think it was because I was there with my car. My uncle is gay and has a partner and they are jealous of me wanting to be a part of his life. Because if I had the chance, I'm sure the boy would want to hang out with me more than them. So, it ends up that my whole damn trip was for nothing, my boy wasn't even going to be there. I felt a little crushed about the whole ordeal, braving the storm to see the kid just to have my uncle's bail because of a chance of weather. I got over the fact that the boy wasn't going to be there and decided to make the best of it. Knowing that my son wasn't going to be around, I then knew that

I could have a day of drinking in excess. So, I at least had that going for me.

I started the day off with a stiff drink and coffee. It was very nice having the cute blonde in the camp site over because I could watch her in her morning routine. She had something special about her, full of energy. I myself am a bit of a bear in the mornings till I at least have a cup of coffee or other drink of choice, hell if I woke up to a beautiful woman like that, I bet I would be a little spunkier in the morning myself. I sat and fantasized about her for a little while till my nephew came and snapped me out of my daydream to ask if I would go to the river with them so that they could swim. I said ok, because I like to see the children enjoying themselves. I miss the days of no care in the world other than to have fun and seek adventure. I sat there wishing that my son was there, but at least I had my family with me. The morning went slow till we got on the bus to go up the river and start our float. The bus driver arrived, and it was an old man who had worked there for years, if I can remember. H doesn't say much, but he takes your ticket and asks you to take a seat. The man will smoke a few filterless cigarettes as he drives, it's like Deja Vu every year, but the quiet old man seems satisfied with his job. They drop us off about fifteen miles upriver from our campsite and you float back to the camp grounds. The place we launch is a small rock bluff and depending on the level of the water, it is an easy spot to launch from. There is a lot of excitement in the minutes before getting on the river, it's a great sense of adventure to let mother nature carry you back to the safety of the camp. The river is easy-going except for a few places with some small rapids or the occasional tree across the river. I always enjoy sitting on the first curve of the river to watch the amateurs come through. There is a bluff in the curve that has a ten-foot overhang you go under, but if you don't judge it right, the current will pull you right under the ledge. It's quite entertaining to watch people crash in the first curve. It's a good thing though, to wake people up because a river is a very dangerous place and people underestimate the fury it can have. But having an intense first curve wakes people up to the real dangers. The river though, truly is a mild experience, not too fast it's truly a lazy river, but the danger is always present.

Everyone tends to drink quite a bit of alcohol, but I could never really get that drunk in the summer heat like that, but I can make a valiant effort trying. I like to take the trip slow, stopping frequently on a sand bar for a quick swim and letting the rest of the group catch up. I mostly waited for my sister and her boyfriend to catch up. They had brought their family along, consisting of all my nieces and nephews. I enjoyed staying close to them, it was their first trip and they seemed to enjoy themselves, especially the kids. Watching them made me remember the first time my dad brought me and my brothers to the river and the amount of fun that we had. My sister's oldest son, who was about twelve or so, had his own kayak. You could see the sense of independence he felt maneuvering his own vessel through the water. The younger kids were spread out between the adult's canoes. They seemed to have just as much fun watching the large carp swim beneath the boats, taking the occasional swing at one with their paddles. They were never fast enough or accurate enough to hit the fish but watching them try was quite entertaining.

The water is very clear, and the visibility is about four feet or so. Every now and then, you can see the occasional turtle running the bottom or even one jumping off a nearby log. Once I saw about ten turtles on the same log all sunbathing and as I neared it, they all started diving off one by one, as if they were on a swim team. Sometimes you will come to calm spots in the river where the water hardly flows. It looked almost like glass where if the wind was blowing in your face, it could turn your boat and blow you back upstream. In these calm spots, the alligator gar would hit the top of the water all around you. Making load-smacking sounds as they reached the surface. Going after whatever food they tried to catch. One can really get lost in the sounds and serenity of nature. All you can hear is the water flowing slowly, the cicadas in the trees all around singing their songs with the other insects,as well as the occasional hawk screeching in the distance. That is one of my favorite things about going to the river is the true serenity you can get being in nature.

Truly forgetting oneself and all the responsibilities in this world it's a magical experience of sorts. To be able to leave the reality, they try to keep us in, like we are slaves to the whole bullshit game of life. I love when I can leave that place and get back to the primitive nature of man that we each have buried in our souls, to be one with nature and to feel the presence of nature around. It can put off great energy if you know how to tap into it. Nature is a very strong element in the fact that if a man was to be wiped from the earth, nature would thrive thru. If you have ever seen an old house that has been abandoned, you know exactly what I'm talking about, the trees and plants slowly take over the structure and animals begin to inhabit it as their own. But nature does not care about upkeep and it slowly erases the presence of man, completely hiding the past. If we were all to leave the planet in only a couple hundred years, there would be almost no trace of human life. Any chance I get though, I try to enjoy nature, it has a healing effect on the soul that so many people miss out on today. I really feel people rob themselves of this feeling by not making any effort to get back to these basic principles that are inside us all. It's sad to watch humanity ignore the things that keep us alive.

After the stretch of calm river, I and my family came to another faster section. It's a sharp left curve that comes around a hundred-plus foot bluff on the outside of the curve. There is a nice hollow in the bend. It's a nice little fishing hole. I have caught several fish there in the past. When you catch the left, there is another good spot for a swim. The kids always enjoy the spot because the current is so fast-flowing through the spot, so they like to run upstream to jump in and float down, repeating this several times. I always enjoyed it myself when I was their age.

I was sitting back on the bank when suddenly here comes the cute blonde from camp and her family floating by. My, how she looked in the red swimsuit, again I acted as if I didn't see her. Luckily, I had my shades on to block her view of my gazing at her as she floated by. Her father waved at me as they floated by me, knowing he saw me looking at his daughter, but he didn't seem to care. He almost was inviting me to join them. I probably should have, I waited five or ten minutes with my family for them to leave, but they were not ready, so I shoved off alone to hopefully catch up with the young blonde and her family. I left too late to catch up with them. My family saw me push off, so they shoved off right after. One of our favorite cliffs to jump from was not too far, so I knew my chance of catching the blonde was lost because we always stopped at the bluff for an hour or so to eat lunch and enjoy the view and the boulder we jumped from. There is a tree that grows from the top of the boulder you could jump from if you were the adventurous type. If you wanted to hike through the woods a bit, you could climb the two-hundred-foot cliff and get to the top. Only if you could manage to scale a few amateur rock faces on the way up. The view from the top was well worth the risk of the climb. You could see for miles down the river from the peak. One time, we climbed to the top and I and my brothers managed to disturb some wasps on the way up. Not even one of us managed to get away without a sting. It was not very fun, but the cool water cooled the pain from the stings. It was a very relaxing spot to take a break. Some people drove to the spot to spend the whole day there just to hang out. It would have been nice to be able to show my son the place.

I took my time hiking back down the cliff, enjoying the sights. You must hike through a small cave area on the way down and many people have stopped and carved their names into the sandstone cliffs. There were many names that scattered the walls. I was thinking about the native Americans and primitive cave drawings of buffalo and deer. I pictured a great one of primitive people hunting the animals in a great show of art. I envisioned the art in movement and watched the whole hunt unfold in my imagination even though there were no drawings, just the names of folks who had passed through the place. The place held a spiritual aspect in my life because I can always go there to escape. The whole river, as a matter of fact, is sacred to me, full of great places where I can find peace. There are not too many places out there like this anymore, every man should have places like this where he can sit in peace with no outer influences to bother him. People tend to move too fast anymore. I prefer to live at the pace of the river, mostly calm but with new excitement around every curve you manage to make it around. The curves are like days, if you make it to the next, you gain the skills and experiences to use to your advantage for the next one.

I reached the bottom of the bluff and took one more jump off the rock into the river, counting the seconds to hit the water and counting the seconds you spend under the water. That is my favorite part of the plunge, the fear of death if you don't come back up. The few seconds of the cold waters in the deepest depths of the river. A truly great feeling as well as when you breach the water's surface and catch that first breath of fresh air. I swam across the river fighting the current under the cliff. I made it back in my canoe to push off for the final leg of the journey. I still had one more area that was dear to me and it was a spring flowing into the main river. I found it one year by complete accident, the water that runs from this stream is cold as ice, even in the dead of summer, it is about ten or twenty degrees colder than the main channel. The water is as clear as glass, the clearest water I have ever seen; it's a great spot to hang out and relax. If you hike up the spring a bit, there is a waterfall with a small pool underneath it. Some years, small fish swim in the pool as you sit and cool off. The waterfall is only about ten feet high, but if you climb to the top and look at the rock it flows over, it has huge grooves cut into them. In some spots, the grooves are cut two to three feet deep in the rock slab. The time it must have taken for the water to carve out the rocks must have been a couple of thousand years or so. The stream splits into different channels and it looks like the ruffles of a fine silk dress carved in stone. It's a beautiful sight to see something nature created like that. It feels like a dream when you see it in person. Amazing how mother nature can produce something like that. I truly love that spot. I even drink the water there straight from the source. It has a pure taste. To me, this is one of the sacred springs the native Americans talked about. A stream of magical properties. The place itself has a certain serenity about it. Once I left, I felt very refreshed, almost blessed if I must try to explain myself. It's back in some very low hanging trees that almost form a tunnel around you. As I walked out of the trees, there was a light at the end of the tunnel. When I stepped out, it was if I walked into a completely different world, almost as if I had left the earth for the time that I spent there. Now that I look back at it, I wish I could have stayed there forever. If only I had a wife with me and a piece of land like that, I would never leave the place.

Finally, back on the main channel of the river, my sister and her kids were sitting on the opposite bank from where the stream was, so I paddled to catch back up with them. It felt like I was in the spring for hours, but I think it was only about fifteen minutes. My sister looked at me kind of funny and asked me where I had been. I told her about the spring, but she showed no interest in it, so we left. We didn't have much further to go now, maybe another mile or so tops till the half way point where you could get out early if you like. If you don't reach it by a certain time, they make you get out so you don't float after dark. We have only made it the whole way a few times and when we did, we had to paddle hard to make it back to camp before dark. We came up to the halfway point and there is about a five hundred yard stretch of river that is very rough if the water is low and of course it was. It takes a considerate amount of skill to pilot through the area without tipping your canoe or getting high centered on some of the large rocks. This is no fun because then you must get out to pull your boat over the obstacles while the rough current rushes by. It's a good place to bust your ass or your shins on the jagged rocks. We all seemed to navigate through just fine.

We reached the landing and we all got out and waited for the bus to pick us up. The river can take a toll on people. Some get sunburned so bad they will regret it for days after. The kids get so tired from paddling all day they have little energy by the time it takes to get back to camp and quickly fall asleep. Some of the adults have drunk themselves belligerent and are lucky to get back into camp before passing out. Some will even pass out on the bus ride home. I myself was right in the middle, slightly drunk and slightly worn out. We boarded the bus home and again, we had a bus driver who had worked there forever. He's an old hippie-looking guy, one of those guys who was stuck in Woodstock never to come out of it. The man had long hair and a goofy attitude, probably from smoking the biggest joint you could imagine, but he greeted everyone with a smile and was a very pleasant man, unlike most people today, he was a real freak from the past. One who was just living to get by and enjoy the ride doing so. I always wished more people would follow in this man's footsteps. People could learn great social skills from a man like that. I would not take any driving pointers from the man, though.

The road out of the halfway point that led to the main road was unpaved and washed out. The driver didn't seem to notice as he pushed the bus about forty miles per hour down the road. I couldn't tell if he was oblivious to the conditions or if he was just trying to wake the drunks, so he wouldn't have to back to camp. The ruts in the road were almost launching the kids clear to the roof of the bus. They seemed to enjoy the tossing and turning and bumping around. As I looked around the bus, the drunks were the complete opposite, as if they were out at sea and the waves were getting the best of them, turning green from the constant movement and trying to hold back the vomit just looking for the nearest place to spew their guts all around. God, I hope we make it back to camp before one of these time bombs of unstable stomach waste explodes, causing a chain reaction of puke and panic. I had a vision of great catastrophe of vile everywhere and people very unhappy luckily, we reached the paved road and the ride smoothed out. There was a sigh of relief as the bus was no longer unstable and rocking out of control.

I think the bus was close to its last day of service from being driven so hard. We were back on the hilly roads where the Buicks belts were suffering so bad on. They seemed to take a pretty good toll on the bus's transmission on the steep climbs, it would not shift out of gear and the engine was screaming away at a million rpm. I had to fight the urge to yell "SHE WONT TAKE THIS ABUSE MUCH LONGER CAPTAIN" but I held myself back. I could feel the bus's relief when we reached the top of the hill and began the descent, but the ride down was not without stress as the driver never seemed to even as much tap the breaks screaming down the hill. I thought we were going to be on two wheels as we went into a few of the curves. We finally made it back to camp, I looked around the bus and had never seen an uglier-looking group of people. Some were white as a ghost from the pure fright of the high-speed bus ride, some green about to hurl their whole days' worth of food and beer all over the place and some so red from the sun that you couldn't tell if they were close to death and sickness or cared beyond belief. Believe me, they were an ugly group or S.O.B.s ready to flee off the bus like pigs in a coral. The bastards even smelt like pigs, they stumbled out one by one with no problem. When I finally reached the door, I was relieved the nightmare was over

I walked back to my campsite, most of my family had made it back before me. As I got back to my car, I spotted the blonde girl. She looked a little redder today, getting close to matching the color of her swimsuit. I leaned in my car to get into my cooler for an ice-cold Guinness since I couldn't take them on the river because of the glass bottles. It's probably my favorite beer, so it was a great reward to have a few leftover from the night before.

"HELL" I thought it was time to take it easy, I had one last stogie that I managed to save, I took it out of my case with a book of matches and as I sparked the match to burn off the first few seconds to get to a clean flame, I heard a voice behind me. I spun around in surprise. It was the beautiful blonde's father, and he had come over to talk to me about my car. I lit the cigar and began to tell him the trouble that I had to go through the day before just to get it down there; he laughed and gave me props for driving a seventy-year-old car as a daily driver. His back was turned to his camp and I was trying hard not to gawk at his daughter across the road. He knew I had been looking at her and I think it was his way of giving me his blessing to go talk to her.

I and my family were about to eat, and it looked like they were about to do the same. I sat down and hurried as I ate so I could go next door and talk to the man and his daughter. I was excited to talk to her, it was funny how everything was working out after being disappointed about my son not showing up. Having the thought of talking to the man's daughter was very exciting and, to top it off, I had the old man's blessing, things could not be better!! I walked over, beer in hand and introduced myself to the man's wife and his daughter. They were all sitting around the fire. Her mother was very good-looking and very nice. Her father was part Indian, so that explained her very tan skin. This was the first time I truly got a good look at her, she was more beautiful up close. She had soft features with a beautiful smile; her name was Sarah, which I found strange because my high school crush's name was Sarah. The blonde was about five-foot-tall and maybe a hundred pounds soaking wet. She was wearing very short jean shorts and the bottom of her petite but damn near hung out the bottoms. I had to keep myself from drooling on myself as she walked around the fire. She still had her little red top on, holding in her small supple breasts. As we sat and told each other stories, she went to drink from her beer, she laughed when she was drinking and spilled beer right in-between her breasts. The beer beaded up and slowly ran down between them. She seemed not to notice, but I could not manage to ignore it. When it got past her swimsuit top right between her breasts, it ran down the center of her stomach. She was very toned with hardly any body fat to speak of. The beer ran right into her belly button and I dreamed of sucking it out. She finally noticed and wiped it away and I tried to pretend that I wasn't watching the whole thing take place. I hoped that her dad didn't see me drool a little. We laughed because she caught my eyes on her stomach. When I looked up, we were staring right into each other's eyes. I could feel that she liked the tensions we were sharing. I thought she was going to pounce on me at any minute. She began staring at me with desire in her eyes; I asked her if she wanted to go for a walk in the dark down to the river. She agreed, and her parents said they were going to bed.

I stood up from my chair and put my hand out to help her up, when our hands touched, it was like an electric shock. When she stood up, the light from the fire was dancing on her skin, she was like a goddess standing there before me. It was as if the fire engulfed us and we were the only two creatures in the cold dark night with the fire radiating our feelings for each other. I put my hands on her small waist just above her hip bone and gave her a peck on her lips. Just enough to ignite her imagination for love. I took her by the hand to go to the river. She told me that she feared the dark, but I ensured her if she was with me, nothing in the dark could harm her. She believed in me. We started walking and I was telling her that once you spend enough time in the dark, you will eventually get used to it and your eyes will adjust. I made sure to hold her tight for the first few minutes, so her fear would go away. I could feel becoming more comfortable the further we walked. It was a full moon that night and you could see all the stars around us. I let her hand go because I could tell she had become comfortable as we got closer to the water's edge. There was a coolness in the air which I appreciated greatly. She mentioned that she was getting chilly, so I pulled her close to me to hold her tightly in my arms. I could feel her supple breasts upon my chest, her nipples were hard from the cold. It was exhilarating to pull her against me. I could feel her body pulling the heat out of mine as the two of us helped each other. She needed warmth and we both craved the love that we were lacking.

We sat down at the river's edge and I asked her how often she had the time to sit back and look at the stars. She told me she is very busy all the time and doesn't have much free time to get out. I found us a good spot on the bank with a few rocks, so we could lay back look at the sky. She was laying with her head on my chest. I was curious if she could hear my heartbeat because I could feel my heart rate slowing because of the comfort I felt with her. She was still cold, and she had her leg across my lap. We were one at that point. I started talking to her about the stars and we fell into a deep conversation. I was running my finger slowly down her side studying every curve of her body, the softness of her skin was almost orgasmic. I could feel her getting goosebumps all over from my touch, but she didn't seem to mind. I moved my hand slowly to the back of her swimsuit, it was the kind that ties in the back. I took my time running my hand up and down her spine just barely touching her skin with the softest touch. I worked my way slowly up and down her back and stopped at the thin string that tied her top together. I pulled one of the ends of the bow slowly, seeing if I could undo the knot without her noticing. I had it about half way undone when she asked what I was doing with a smile. I told her not to worry about it in a joking manner, even though she knew damn well what I was up to. I almost had the knot undone when a shooting star went racing across the sky. It seemed to almost stop time and seemed to hang there for an eternity. She popped up with excitement to ask me if I had seen it. As she did, the rest of the knot of the swimsuit top came undone, exposing her breasts. She didn't seem to notice because of the excitement she had from the shooting star. She kicked her leg completely over me, startling me at this point with her top barely hanging on. She asked me if I knew what a shooting star meant, and I told her she had to make a wish, but she couldn't tell anyone, or it wouldn't come true. I asked her if she had made one and she told me she already had as she pulled me close and gave me a kiss with great intensity. Her small naked breasts were pushing firmly against my bare chest now. I could feel her breasts up against my skin, the intensity rose from there. She pulled me up, ripping my Hawaiian shirt the rest of the way off very ferociously with desire. Being careful not to let our lips come apart. She pushed me back to the ground, still startling me with both hands on my chest, grabbing my chest hair with slight force, pulling herself back to my lips and rubbing against me. The energy was extreme and full of passion. She sat up again, flipping her hair back slowly moving her hips on my lap. I then pulled her hair back while she kept moving her hips on my lap. I then pulled her back down to my lips with my hand on the back of her head by her hair. I pulled her head sideways to have access to her neck, which I started to kiss and slightly bite. She quivered with excitement. I sat up with her still on my lap and pulled her head back as to arch the back and started working my way from her neck down to her chest to her beautiful petite breasts making sure to be very thorough in kissing everywhere but her nipples to tease her. I kissed right in the center of her chest, right between each breast. She pulled the back of my head harder into her bosom, almost suffocating me in her chest. I grabbed her by her bottom and went straight for her nipples, as my tongue and lips reached one of them, she would let out a little whimper letting me know she enjoyed every bit. I then firmly grabbed her by the waist and squeezed her waist just above her hips rather firmly. She whispered in my ear that she wanted me repeatedly as she rocked on my lap, vigorously working herself up more and more, frustrating herself because of the layers of fabric between us. She was like a ferocious lioness in the way she flipped her hair back and dug her fingernails hard into my chest.

My favorite trait in a woman is one that knows what she wants with life and doesn't second guess her actions. At that point, we were in the heat of things. We were both half naked already, she hopped up off my lap and stared me straight in the eyes and told me to stand up. She came close to me and embraced me firmly. I picked her up off the ground and held her with her legs around my waist, squeezing me tight we were in a frenzy of love and passion. I set her down and she turned around, looking back at me over her shoulder as she removed her shorts, slowly teasing me with every second she strung out, knowing it was pure torture of desire. Her shorts were halfway down with the red bikini showing over the top of her shorts; it was about a whole ordeal by the time she lost her shorts and kicked the red bikini bottoms off right before my eyes. She was pure beauty standing right before me. She had the moonlight glistening off her naked body. I could live in that moment forever. I stood there in awe as she walked words me slowly. She got within arm's reach and she mischievously smiled as she got close. I put my arms out to pull her close and she pulled down my swimsuit in a flash and came in for another kiss. I managed to kick my leg out of my swimsuit and she hopped on me again. At this point, our bodies were one again. I could feel the warmth of her: she was ready. We laid on the ground once more and she was back on top, she lowered herself onto me, slowly easing me inside of her inch by inch till I was fully inside her. The work to get to this point was well worth the wait. She quivered slightly with every thrust letting out a slight moan each time she trusted herself down. I could feel the warmth inside her intensify as

36

she moaned load, this time slowing her pace. I was on the verge of release; we hadn't had time to use a condom, so I had to hold myself back. She was right in my ear as she lowered herself down once more, whispering in my ear, just begging me to let go and not to worry. As soon as she said that, it was an instant release. I was completely paralyzed, hardly even able to breathe as she didn't stop. The warmth of our bodies together was fierce now. We didn't want to let each other go.

We laid there for about an hour, just holding each other. We began talking about what now and we decided it was best if we both went our separate ways since we lived so far away from each other, but we made a vow to try and see each other again someday. That's one of the beauties of spur-of-the-moment love, many times I have left a girl and never seen her again, knowing that we both wanted each other, and we just missed the opportunity to truly get an experience of a lifetime. I wonder every day about women that I have met in the past. I love them all and I will for the rest of my life. I often wonder if there **are** any girls who think of me in the same way. We slept on the bank of the river till the morning with her laying on top of me all night. We woke up just before the sun broke the horizon and walked back to camp, both of us sneaking back into camp. It was Sunday now and the day I was leaving. Sarah and her family were staying another day, but I had to go. I walked over to her and said goodbye. I had my car packed and was ready to leave. I had forgotten that the starter was out, so she watched me crawl under the thing to jump-start it. I drove the car over to the river to get a picture of the family in front of the car as proof of the adventure. We had the whole family together in front of the car to take a picture; all of us were standing in front of the car with the river in the background. It was a good picture.

It's kind of funny because my grandpa had a Buick just like that and he was the original man who started the tradition of going to Tahlequah. It was like he was there with the family watching over us and me especially making sure the old car made it the whole way. He was a major influence on me and helped me get the mindset I have now, the one to be mechanically inclined and to fix things that are broken instead of just throwing things out. I try to live my life like that, fix and save things and preserve history as much as possible, as well as family values that we have lost over the years.

After we took the picture and said our goodbyes, I decided to try and break the tires free for the first time. After all, it was one of the tops of the line models and the first year of the v8. It was a true hotrod for its day. I tore out of the campsite doing a victory lap throwing gravel around every corner, fishtailing all over the place. It was like a scene from an old moonshine movie, watching them outrun the police. I felt like I had a successful trip. I felt good about the ride home and decided to take a long way home I chose the path to take time and sit back and enjoy the drive and the unknown scenery.

"SOMETIMES THE ROADS LESS TRAVELED LEAD TO BETTER PATHS THAN YOU COULD EVER IMAGINE"

5

HAVING GUESTS ON THE BOAT

Finally, what a relief back to the lake and even better, I have company. I used to know her from high school, an old acquaintance. I had a bit of a thing for her. She's a beautiful thing, very thin and petite, maybe a hundred pounds dripping wet and oh, how she looked good dripping wet. She messaged me out of the blue to see what I was up to and with little convincing, she decided to come out to the boat. It turned into about a week's stay. I hopped on the Goldwing 1100, a beast of a motorcycle and pointed it backward to Kansas City and pulled the throttle to the max. I picked her up at her house after not seeing her in two or three years. As I pulled up, I had a little nervousness about myself. I always get enjoyment out of that little uneasy feeling. It's one of those childhood feelings that I don't get very much anymore, just that sense of nervousness you get when you have a crush on a girl and are about to talk to her. Waiting out front, she opened her garage door and I saw her again after a long time. She was just as I remembered her, very cute and very beautiful, ache walked towards me and the nervousness went away. She was all smiles, it was a relief. She told me we needed to take out of there quickly before her dad decided to come out. We zipped out of there and decided to stop for a few minutes before jumping on the highway and smoking a cigarette. I always liked a girl who smokes cigarettes, there's something elegant about it, it reminds me of the old-time movie stars, where women smoked with their red lipstick on. I knew that we were going to have a good time at that point because I parked the motorcycle kind in the middle of the road and we sat on the curb smoking as we watched people drive by, cursing us for blocking the road. We just sat back and laughed and caught up with each other's past, then we decided to hit the road. It's a fourth five-minute ride to the lake from Kansas City. It was getting kind of dark, but I could see our shadows racing us on the pavement as we cruised in the night. She has something wild about her a free spirit and a simple girl. She's one of those girls that if you want to capture her, you have to offer her a regular dose of excitement to take her into her wild side: a true nature lover and a woman of peace.

As we pulled up to the marina, I was a little nervous about what she might have thought of the boat also a little nervous whether or not the thing was going to act upon me. To my surprise, the thing fired right up and off we were to find a nice cove for the night. We made it across the lake with no problems and anchored up to cook some dinner. I cooked her chicken fajitas with red and green peppers; she seemed satisfied with the food, I myself thought that it was very good. We sat around drinking and catching up with each other till I came up with an idea. I made a bet with her that she would not jump into the lake for a hundred dollars. You must remember it was now the start of October, so the weather was rather cool, but the water temperature was still warm. I got her to consider the idea and it was quite fun watching her preparing herself for the plunge into the dark water. She finally made up her mind and she was going to do it; she stood up and began to remove her clothes. This was quite exciting, a girl of this caliber stripping down slowly right in front of me, still deciding whether she was going to do it or not. As she stood there naked, I decided that I wasn't going to let her go in alone, so I began to get undressed as well. She walked to the back of the boat to take the plunge, with me following right behind. I figured that she was going to psych herself out on the swim deck, but to my surprise, she jumped right in, pulling me with her. She hit the water and when she came up, she shrieked a little she was back to the swim ladder faster than I thought even possible. As she got out of the water, she stood there stark naked, as naked as the night's sky with no clouds in sight. As she stood in front of me, you could see the reflection of the stars glistening off her petite wet body and her nipples were as sharp as tacks, a sight of pure beauty standing before me. We were both naked still and I walked onto the boat to get her a towel and held her close. I got my first kiss after that, it was something special. I always like a woman that will share the unordinary adventures with me. She jokingly asked about the hundred dollars and when I told her that I would have to write her an I.O.U. she laughed, and we decided to go crawl into the warm bed.

The next morning, we woke up and I got out of bed to make some coffee for us to drink and she insisted on making me some oatmeal. Like I said earlier, there's nothing better than a good boat girl. I got to lay in bed while she made me breakfast half-naked. It was some of the best oatmeal I have ever eaten. After breakfast, we continued to drink coffee and I convinced her to come out to the back of the boat, still only half-dressed, we continued to enjoy the morning stark naked. One of my favorite things about the boat is you don't have any newborns to spy on you when you have a nice spot in a cove; these are some of my favorite times, early mornings. Sometimes I like to fish stark naked off the front of the boat; the freedom of this is a feeling you cannot explain, it's something you just must experience on your own. Especially if you're with a girl it's nice being naked around a good woman when there's no judgment between the two of you and you can both be comfortable in this manner. It's a primitive ordeal we came into the world like this, so damnit, why not enjoy how the world was created? The human body is a beautiful thing, in my opinion. Especially Brooklyn on this morning, she looked very natural in this state, like that's where she was supposed to be at that moment in time out there with a wild man like myself, trying to get her to open to the true feeling of being alive. I like to find ways of getting this feeling back whenever I can and what better way of that than being naked with a beautiful girl holding each other close and feeling the warmth of each other's body and the heat from the sun warming your skin. A sense of becoming one between two people is a sense of magic or enlightenment. I wish I had a model sometimes where I could study her features and create a sculpture or a painting or hell, even to just look at her beauty. Women are strange creatures; they are the creators of life, that's what intrigues me the most about them. I really hate how society portrays women today because, in my opinion, all women are beautiful, it doesn't matter shape or size, they all have their good points about them, whether they have a beautiful heart or personality or even something as simple as a cute smile. Some of them more than others, radiate like the sun radiates heat on the earth. Those are the women I'm attracted to the most, the true lovers, they are getting harder to find these days, but they are still out there.

It was quite windy on the lake that morning, with white caps across the lake. The boat was rocking fiercely and not just because of the morning activities. The waves in the lake were bobbing the boat up and down and with each wave, the anchor was moving across the bottom, sending the boat drifting across the lake slightly with each one. We were the only ones crazy enough to be on the lake at that time, but we were on a fine boat for it, she took the waves well. We were rocking pretty good as we floated out to the main channel of the lake. Brooklyn didn't seem to mind and that's what I like about her. She doesn't seem to get worked even in the thick of it. We decided to head back to the marina for a little while, so I went to fire the boat up. She cranked right over, so we started our journey across the lake as we got out in the middle, the waves were more like the ocean than a lake, it was quite fun, having never been in rough water like that before. We had made it about two-thirds of the way across the lake when the engine died out. "SHIT" I thought, perfect weather for the damn thing to break down right in the worst of the waves on the lake. I looked at Brooklyn feeling a little uneasy about the situation, but she seemed calm as could be. I threw the anchor and began working on the boat. I feel as if she took pleasure in watching me work on the thing. I feel it helped her stay relaxed because I had a pretty good idea of what I was doing, having gotten myself out of a few predicaments prior to the arrival. After little work, I managed to get the boat fired up again and once again, we were on our way. I was thinking to myself, great, she probably thinks this boat is a piece of shit, how it keeps dying and me having to work on it just to get across the lake. The wind and the waves were still fierce, and I had the anchor set well I needed to have Brooklyn drive the boat words the anchor, so I could pull it off the bottom. This turned into a hysterical ordeal because she had never driven a boat before and couldn't quite grasp the concept, but I managed to maintain my composure. I was getting frustrated with her not being able to drive the boat, but I guess it's a foreign concept to most people. I asked her to cut it to the right little and then to the left, but she would crank the wheel all the way and spin the boat severely instead of a gradual turn. I eventually managed to get the anchor up and took the controls back from her.

We had almost made it back to the marina and we were getting close to the wave break around the place, maybe a hundred yards out and the boat died out again. This time the engine would not crank at all when I turned the key. I had never had this problem before, so it puzzled me. I was forced to throw the anchor once more, but the waves and the rock bottom of the lake made it impossible for the anchor to bite. I frantically ran around the boat trying to get the thing fired back up I even tried both keys and nothing at either driving station. It was a harsh tease because we were so close I grabbed the anchor rope and could feel that it was just skipping across the bottom and we were headed straight for a shallow cove. I was seriously concerned at this point. I tried the key once more and still nothing. As we got closer to the shallows, I tried to raise the lower unit, so it would not hit the ground, but it wouldn't work either. We got blown into the beach and the lower unit dug into the ground with the bow of the boat facing the shore, each wave crashing into the stern, pushing us further and further onto the beach. The waves were crashing up over the back of the boat like the movie jaws when the

43

boat is being pulled backwards by the shark, but we didn't have a rope to cut. I was getting worried about the boat sinking at this point from the amount of water that was coming over the back. It was quite exciting. I thought maybe my dream was coming true of sinking the boat. I had to pull the engine cover to see about getting the thing running and as I was down in the belly of the thing, the water kept crashing over the back, soaking me more and more. I eventually found the problem and the batteries had come loose in the rough seas, so that explained my power loss. I hooked the wire back up and at last, I had power back. I climbed up top to raise the lower unit so that it wasn't digging in the ground and it shot up with ease, the boat then spun around with the bow facing out words the lake, but the waves kept pushing us further and further on shore. Luckily it was a mud bottom at that spot, so there were no real worries of damaging the boat. I tried to hop out of the boat and pull us by hand back out into deeper water, but the waves and the wind were just too great of a match for me to pull the thing by myself. I didn't want to ask Brooklyn to get out and help either, but it's not like her fragile one-hundred-pound frame would have helped much.

Finally, I decided that we were stuck. We managed to make the best of it though we were only about thirty or fourth feet from the bank, so we could hop off the boat easily and walk ashore. We laughed at the fact that we had our own private beach now. We then were forced to figure out what to do now, well more or less, I was forced to try and figure something out. I walked into the woods, where I found a trail right past the tree line, so at least we had a pretty good path to get back on. We decided to walk back to my van after I decided I needed to get some help from my brother or dad to push the boat back off the shore.

I really got to see the adventurous side of Brooklyn on our walk back. We were both bare foot and it was a two-mile hike back to the car. Now I typically am barefoot all summer long, but I don't think Brooklyn does the same, but she carried her shoes the whole way back, I was extremely impressed. We got about half way back and Brooklyn took off in a sprint. I followed of course, and it almost felt as if we were two deer running through the woods. She ran with grace, hardly making a sound as her feet seemed to barely touch the ground. She almost floated; it was a graceful stride that I couldn't explain, I just tried to keep up. We made our way down the trail where we had to cut through the woods to get us out to a field next to the parking lot. As we walked out into the field, there was a certain serenity about watching the field of tall grass blow in the wind like waves on the ocean. I made sure to mark the place where we came out of the woods, so we could find our way back. I marked it by remembering a tree that split in two like two lost friends standing next to each other, watching over the vast field of grass.

I connected with this girl; she has a bit of wildness buried deep within her roots and when they come out, she is something amazing, a true wild woman. Every woman has this primitive wild side in them and it is just waiting for someone or something to help them bring it out of them. To give a girl the opportunity to let loose of this inner wild child that is inside us all is my favorite thing in the world. This is the sort of feeling I chase, the feeling of freedom. Society, as I see it, strips us from this true wild beast or inner child that is in us all. The city lights take away the stars and our work schedules take away our time to have more experiences. We are wild people and we need to find more ways to get us back to these ancient roots and learn how to get tribble again. Things as simple as a campfire with good music and friends or something as simple as looking up at the sky or even just lying in a field of tall grass watching the clouds roll by. As we finally made it back to the car, we hopped in and headed back to the city for more food and supplies also so I could tell my dad that I had managed to get the boat stuck.

We also picked up an extra hand her dog; he is a white Pitbull with a bit of black mixed in, a good-looking dog, very strong and attentive, good qualities that I look for in a dog. We got back as it was starting to get dark and there was a storm brewing on the horizon full of fierce lightning zigging through it like wild fire. I was getting nervous about the rain coming in on us on the hike back to the boat. We had to find the spot in the field before it got dark and once we were on the trail, we would be fine the rest of the way. Again, we made the hike barefoot; she stopped me, saying that she had stepped on a thorn and I began to look at her foot, she said the hell with it and we just continued our way back, navigating the dark trails with only one flash light. I was watching the dog and he seemed to be on our trail, so I took faith in him to navigate the few forks in the trail we encountered. It's funny how a dog purely by their nose can get us back to the boat, having never been there in the first place. Man has a pretty good nose as well; there have been times bird hunting where I have gotten a kill and been able to smell the blood of the animal in the field. Our nose is blind in the city, there are no pure smells as we are constantly breathing unsure smells that the city produces. Again, all our primitive abilities have been lost to the creation of cities and money. We are no longer able to tap into these primitive instincts. It's just the production of a breed of emotionless beings that are unhappy and don't have a drive to fight because they have all sold off these feelings to keep up with some family they call the jounces with their cars, TVs, and video games catered too by the luxuries that man has created that have drained us of our true wild drive. Maybe this drive I talk about is just so old that it is forgotten in time and it has never really crossed their minds at all. Maybe I'm just one of the few who has this drive still in me. I try to keep it going for the rest of us. Tapping into it is easy if you try, it's as simple as sitting in the woods to set off your mind from all the bullshit around and focusing on the real things the birds and trees around being quiet enough that the animals don't even know that you are there anymore as they start to come close to you. The birds that fly around you are singing their songs and the squills come back out to play. The peace I have found in this type of meditation can truly bring out the animal living inside us all. If you have never experienced this before, you will never truly understand the serenity of it. A sense of true beauty in the world again. It can take me back to a simpler time in life and being a child no longer care in the world. At that point, your true senses kick in the sense of smell and sound is heightened to a state you never realized you have. Every person is filled with these senses, they just don't know they exist because they have never got the tribal experience of it all, not knowing how to shut everything down to become at peace with the world.

Finally, after finding our way through the dark trails and back to the boat, we decided to light a fire on our own private beach for the night. I wished that I had a drum to pound on throughout the night while we sat and watched the fire. We sat back and watched the boat laying on its side and we had no care at all, just the two of us, a fire and a beached boat. But then, right there was finding true life and loving every minute of it. There was something beautiful about fighting the wind and the water to wind up on a personal beach just for the two of us. If it wasn't for me taking chances, I would not have much of a story to tell. I try to keep this drive in me to push myself to higher levels. "LIFES A BITCH SOMETIMES" but if you take it as it comes, sometimes it's not that bad. If you never leave the safeties of society, you will never truly live. Get out there and fight your fights, the real ones, not the ones in your video games. We all have a life path that can be altered very easily if you try to change it up. You must search all the way back to your true roots to finally find your starting point. As people sit at their homes watching TV, the real world is passing us all by. It's a spiritual thing to sit in front of a fire just to watch it dance, twirling and whipping around forming minia-ture tornados, the fire can dance a fierce dance in the night. When you can see the pure energy in a fire, it can warm you to your core and in rough circumstances, that's the only thing keeping you alive, it truly is life itself. There's a certain amount of respect to be had for it. Smoke and fire together are a beautiful thing, it is one thing that can bring people together to sit around and share stories. We had a good night sitting around the fire and we sat till we both felt too cold. I could have put more wood on the fire, but we let the night get away with us and we decided to go to bed.

The next morning, I got up and I made coffee. I decided to take the dog for a walk around the bank and Brooklyn decided to stay on the boat and take it easy. As I walked around the bank, I found many large feathers Strewn all around the place; they were beautiful things fit for an Indian headdress. I began picking them up and started picking up trash as I walked along. I found all sorts of cool treasures around the lake, the night before, I found a piece of driftwood on the water's edge and when I shone a light on it, its shadow resembled the shape of a wolf howling at the moon perfectly. An artist could not have painted a better picture. I thought it was cool because Brooklyn had a wolf tattoo and I had talked to Brooklyn about howling at the moon the night before. It's amazing what nature has to offer when you have the time to get back to it. I myself just quit jobs and do side work so I can take the time to get back to nature. I took all my findings back to the boat to eat breakfast; Brooklyn again had it made by the time I came back to the boat and it must have been a tricky feat to accomplish because the boat was listing to one side heavily. We hung out the rest of the day while I tried to get the boat out and failed in many attempts. With no luck getting the boat out, I decided to take a break and I threw a couple of poles out in the water and I managed to catch a good pan-sized catfish only a few minutes later. Brooklyn decided to cook rice for dinner and I thought that I would cook the fish as a side. God had granted me a fish, so I knew that someone was looking out for me at least. I ate dinner with a large smile on my face, eating my dinner that was provided by the land, there's nothing better than that. While we were sitting there eating dinner, I heard my catfish pole ringing again, but I was eating, so I let it ring, knowing that I had one hooked pretty good. As I ignored it, the pole began to bang hard off the side of the boat and I could ignore it no longer. I got up, knowing that it was a good-sized fish by the sound of the pole on the side of the boat. It was the best fish I had caught so far, a four or five pounder. So even in the thick of it all, I could still catch fish. The forces were against me and I still managed to find peace in the simple things.

We decided to leave the lake because I couldn't get it off the bank, so I let the catfish go to catch another day. On the way back home, I was still pondering how to get the thing off the bank. I ended up recruiting my old man and my brother. I got lucky though, because good old mother nature decided to help. It rained the day before we got back out, raising the lake just enough where the boat had more water under it to help us get the thing out. It made it a breeze to get it off, but there was another problem. When we showed up, the boat had sunk and was full of water about two feet deep in the bottom. It managed to come up over the carpet about six inches staining the carpet a brown color. I found out that I had an exhaust hose pop off when the lower unit hit the ground and it made the boat spring a leak. In the day and a half that I was away, the boat managed to fill with water. I fixed the exhaust hose leak and we kicked the pumps on and the thing pumped out just fine, slowly floating once more. We then had to push the boat off the shore and I fired the engine up and it purred like a kitten and I pulled it into deeper water. I was thankful that my family showed up to help because they made it a lot easier. If not for them, I was planning on digging the damn thing out and it probably would have taken me a whole day to do so by myself, but with their help, I didn't have to. I drove the boat back to the marina and put it back in my slip; the people working seemed relieved that we managed to get it out of there. Finally, I thought back to the reality of living on the lake.

I was a little uneasy about the boat after that because there were a few days of bad weather heading my way and I was still a little uneasy about whether or not I damaged the boat in the ordeal. When I headed back out, though, the boat was still afloat. I stayed the night on the boat because I had made the trip out there and I figured I could get some weighting done in my free time. I made it an early night and woke up to make breakfast and coffee. I put on some Hunter S. Thompson recordings while I worked. As I sat and typed for the day listening to a fellow writer, I always like listening or reading others' work as I write, it helps you grasp the rhythm of the brighter and you can see it unfold on your pages. I myself am not a famous writer and have very minimal experience, so I forget a lot of punctuation. I tend to lose the sense of everything when I write, that's why I enjoy it so much. No time at all to think about proper grammar, if I'm getting words on paper, I'll leave the rest up to the editors reading all my gibberish. I want to see if they can decipher it

49

on their own. Hell, who knows if anyone will ever read any of this anyways, but that's the fun of it all, it truly doesn't matter what I write about as long as I'm enjoying doing it, that's the only thing that really matters to me.

I was hitting a bit of a dry spell when I looked at the counter and I saw the feathers that I had collected the day before and I picked a good one out. I found a bit of string as well. I needed some good juju on the boat after all the calamities of the past few weeks, so I sat down and made a feather pendant for good luck. I wove the string around the quill of the feather and I found a few beads that I found from Brooklyn's stay and I fastened them onto the feather. With the colorful string, it looked just like some sort of native American pendant, "GOOD" I thought, finally some good juju aboard. With no name for the damn thing, I needed to make up for it with things from her surroundings. A vessel should always have things from nature on board to keep the thing safe. Sailors are some of the most supersti-tious folks of them all, so I guess I'll go along with it and do anything to help this boat out.

The main thing that I learned to be Leary of on a boat is mother nature, but sometimes you must test her strengths to see what you can get away with. She can be rough, but she can also take care when you need it, like helping to float my boat with the large rainstorm from the night prior of trying to get it out. She takes care of the ones who take care of her, dealing with nature is a bit of a one-on-one fight. She's a tough one to deal with, but there's something about enduring her fury she can bring. She can really bring a man to peace though, knowing that he can endure and survive new obstacles thrown at him by mother nature, she is very unpredictable. If you want to become a man, get out and hang out with mother nature, she can teach you more in one day than you can learn in a week. Being out in her beauties and her mysteries can bring a man back down to earth and back to himself. It's a true test of grit for all of you who don't know what that is, it means you can withstand the storm.

6

GONE FISHING

I had talked to my good friend Mike Myers about coming out to the boat and we set a date to go out and do a bit of fishing. I had to go into town to get some chicken livers that morning. Mike wasn't coming out till about noon, so this gave me plenty of time to go into town to get some shopping done. I left the boat and went to fire the old 53 Buick up. She started with ease and I drove into town. I needed to get gas in the car and I always filled a five-gallon can for the boat every time I went to town. As I pulled into the gas station, there was a beautiful 40s ford convertible with the hood up at a pump. As I stepped out of the car, I asked the old man if he had a problem and he told me that his battery had run down on him and asked if I could give him a jump. I told him I would be happy too as soon as I got done filling my car with fuel. He thanked me and waited for me to get done fueling up. I pulled the old Buick to the front of his car and hooked up the wires. I was missing an end on one of the cords, so I had to hold it on my battery, but I told the man it should work. He went to turn the thing over and it fired right up. He came over and shook my hand to thank me for the jump and asked him if I was heading to the car show. I asked him what show, and he looked at me surprised. He then told me that he figured I knew about the show driving my car, but I told him that it was my daily driver and he laughed, handing me a pamphlet for the show before he left.

I ran into the gas station to buy a pack of smokes and I decided I was going to check the show out for a little while. I had a few hours to kill before I had to meet Mike back at the boat. I hoped in and drove into the town of Lawrence, Kansas, and to my surprise, it was a huge car show, maybe five hundred cars or so. I had to go get my registration ticket to put my car in the show and drove to the entrance and to my surprise, the man letting people in gave me a front-row spot. My car was literally the first one in the gates. I left my car with the keys in the ignition because I never take them out of the thing. I like to keep faith in humanity and not worried about someone trying to steal my car, but I went to look at the other cars in the show. There were many old muscle cars all around. I enjoy the Oldtimers car shows because you can look under the hood and see what they are running and their carb setups and what have you. There were many beautiful cars there and a 1920s Buick truck caught my eye, probably the oldest car there and I looked it over well. It was an all-original truck, just like it was from the factory, but it had been taken care of extremely well throughout the years. It was by far my favourite car there. The thing wasn't about speed or power, but it was a working man's vehicle built specifically for its job and that was to be a truck. rough around the edges but very well built with good materials. The thing had the original brass radiator on it and exposed pushrods with Babbitt bearings on the engine where you had to oil the engine manually every so many miles or every time you drove it. I walked around looking at every car, there were some of all sorts, from jags to custom kit cars people had built and American muscle from just about every year. I spent about an hour and a half checking everything out, but it was time for me to head out; they had a vote for all the cars there and they would be announcing the winner later on, but I didn't even care if I was to win or not this kind of shows are all about getting together and showing what you have to offer and the work you have put in on your stuff. It's never been about winning to me but just trying and doing the best that I can.

I made my way back to my car and managed to see another Buick like mine in the show i. It was a Buick super but pretty much the same body style, it was done up in the rat rod style and looked very good. When I got back to my car I hopped in and the keys were still in the ignition, ready to drive off. I made my way to the grocery store, where I bought some chicken livers to use as fish bait and headed back to the lake to meet Mike. As I was driving back to the lake and I thought about my grandpa, who I used to go fishing with before he passed, and I could have sworn out of the corner of my eye I saw the old man sitting next to me. After that, I knew the day was going to be good for fishing. When I got back to the marina, Mike was almost there, so I got the boat ready to take out for the day. We pushed off and Mike asked me where we were going to go fish. I told him that I had a spot in mind that I had done pretty good at in the past, but it was clear on the other side of the lake. We both had a beer in hand and I gave him the chance to drive the boat around a little bit on the way to the spot. He seemed to be enjoying himself, it's quite the treat to be on a boat like this and better yet get to drive the thing. As we neared the spot, though, I had to take back over because it was back in some trees and I had a special way to get in the trees and set an anchor to get us in a good spot. We baited the hooks with the liver and chucked our lines out and cracked another beer. It's funny how mike asked about getting the liver blood on the boat and I told him that I didn't care. Most people with a boat like this would probably throw a fit. I hopped in the boat and got some tunes cranking while we waited. It didn't take long for me to hook into my first one. I pulled it up and it was a good two or three pounders. Once I caught it, I cleaned it right there on the swim deck of the boat and threw the meat on a plate and I asked Mike if he wanted fresh fish, he agreed, so I kicked the stove on and filled the pan with oil. We just sat kicking back, drinking beers eating fresh catfish straight out of the lake, nothing better, in my opinion. Good friends, good music, and good eats, the simple things. About ten minutes later, My pole went smoking off the back of the boat and I knew I had another one. Mike, at this point, seemed a little disappointed in not catching anything, so of course I had to bust his balls a little. A few hours and quite a few beers later, we were getting ready to go back in. I was on my way to start the boat and again, my pole went slapping. I chuckled a little and reeled in the third one, but I think my good luck got to me and the fish got off right at the back of the boat. I pulled the anchor and maneuvered the boat back through the trees and we started heading back. I was really opening the boat up and I got close to the main channel when I hit bottom again, breaking the fins off the prop. We came to a stop and luckily, I had a second prop learning from my previous mistakes. I jumped off the back of the boat and had the old one off and the new one on in about ten minutes flat. Mike seemed a little bummed that we damaged the boat and I told him that it comes with the territory of dealing with boats and that shit happens to the best of them all. We got to the marina and said our goodbyes.

The old boat is throwing more problems at me left and right, I keep on with it though, because I'm not one to give up easily. I went to take the boat out today and the thing isn't getting fuel today. I made it to the exit of the marina and luckily, the boat died before I got out on the open water. The gas tank has sludge in it and I must keep a hefty supply of fuel filters on board to combat the problem. I slapped a new one on and thought that I solved the problem, so I headed out on the lake. The thing worked till I got about half way across the lake. This was to be another day of fighting the boat, but I really didn't care. The sun was shining bright, so did I, and it was warm, so no complaints from me. I had done some work on the shower that day and I decided to test it out and take a shower out on the lake. The thing worked well, and I stepped into the kitchen of the boat stark naked. It was during the week, so I wasn't worried about anyone else around, so I just hung out naked all day. I went to make lunch and I had the back door of the boat open and to my surprise, there was a man on a small sailboat right off the stern. I didn't hear him approach with him using the sails. I turned around and there he was, looking right in the back of my boat. I waved at the man, not really thinking about my nakedness, but he waved back. The name of his boat was the adventure seeker. I put swim trunks on to go on the bow to do some meditation. As I sat there I could hear the man's sails whipping around in the wind with a tattering sound. I sat and meditated to the sound, pretending that I was out on the ocean in the Bahamas somewhere and my sails were flying high, just making my way to who knows where. I think when you find a place like this, there really isn't anything better. I still didn't have the boat fixed, but I had no care in the world as I sat in the middle of the lake with my broken boat. The thing would run, but only for a few minutes at a time, the floats in the carb were sticking. Really once you're out on the lake, the only rule that I have is you leave your worries at the water's edge.

I began to fidget with the boat once more, trying to fix it. The beauty of the thing is I didn't have anything else better to do than to hang out and work on the boat. I managed to limp it back to the dock, but I'm starting to get fed up with this boat. I'm just running into too many problems to fix and I'm starting to feel like I can't fix them all. It's kind of like the world these days. I see all these problems that need addressing, but by the time you fix one another one arises; sometimes, things are just beyond repair, but I try not to lose hope in the thick of it all. I own this damn boat now, so I have to stick with it till the thing works properly, otherwise I might have to just sink the damn thing and I refuse to do so, there must be a way to get things ship-shape once again, but then again maybe not, maybe the thing is unfixable, maybe there is just an unstoppable doom lurking in this boat and maybe with the world too. If we can work on a few things, there's a way to save this thing, the forces are against me, though. When referring to the world though, it's the rich bastards who own the whole thing and they are just waiting to kill us all off. The scary thing I see though, is these well off people don't even realize that the amount of money they have doesn't even come close to the cost of living through the great destruction on its way for this country and for the world. We are at our breaking point for society, like I am with my boat, we are about to be finished and there's nothing that we can do to change this. We are running out of resources and drive in people to try and change anything. People are happy just sitting back and watching the show go on, but the more and more I look at things, we are heading for a great finale with no sequel. I just hope in the end doesn't but the ticket out and that the true lovers of the world get the chance to make a difference. I would hate to see the world run by dirty money, there's no chance for survival if this happens. I hope if the show is at its end, the whole shithouse goes up in flames because everyone deserves a fair chance. Some of the best people in the world that I have met have nothing. They learn to be happy like this, not with materialistic things and greed. I try not to be so negative like this, but the more I see, the more irritated I get about the imminent doom. But hell, we live like we are all slaves, so maybe we can have a chance at living as real people once more. I hope if I come back to this world once more, it will be a better place next time around, I don't want to come back to see any more pain and suffering; I can't take it anymore, to see the people looking like they are dead. It's sad to see this in the people, soulless and nothing that they can do to change. We are a generation of death, our livelihood slowly getting ripped out of us all piece by piece. I see this in people and it drives me to the point of insanity because it seems like no one else can see a true pure life, it's so far from reality, it's not even right. Our primitive drive is out of us. It's sad money rules over our drive, no longer the sense of truly living, it makes me sick to my stomach to think about it. But that's enough of my negative rants, I'm on a path to enlighten-ment to search for my own and others' true inner beings to find the drive that is being stolen from all of us. Hopefully, someone other than I will decide to fight for a good cause once again.

It's the end of the lake season damnit it's just getting too cold to stay out on this god-forsaken boat of mine. I still haven't managed to get the damn thing running again. The marina is running up my tab because I can't take it out my slip. Bastards, I thought. I told them about my predicament and you would think they would give a man a break. The damn boat has been fun for the year, but it's starting to nickel and dime me to damn near bankruptcy. The next payment for the slip is due and I don't have the cash, so I got to get this damn thing out of the water before they decide to charge me again. Luckily,

I had found the small skiff for my old man and he managed to get the thing running a few weeks before, so I asked him to come out and pull the damn boat to the dock, so I could pull it out of the lake and winterize the damn thing. My dad's boat is just a tiny skiff, about twelve-foot-long and I didn't think the little boat would be able to pull and maneuver the twenty-five-foot cabin cruiser, but we lucked out with no wind and we managed to get the boat safely to the dock, finally, I thought I'm done with this damn monstrosity of a problem for the year. The water was too cold to swim anyway, so it was about that time. Luckily though, any of the problems the thing had were all easy to fix, but no more worries the rest of the year and the marina only charges sixty dollars a month to store the thing, so not too bad. Also, the old trusty van didn't let me down and pulled the boat from the lake with no problems, but getting the boat out means I must go back to the old grind of living with my old man and stepmom and back to the everyday life of every living soul in this country. The soul-sucking reality we are all forced to live. Damn, I wished the summer never ended. I would rather fight an old boat every day than fight the monotony of this god-forsaken city of ours. Hell, a bad day on the boat is better than a good day in the city. I have a lot more peace and my weighting is a lot better and more peaceful on the water or in nature. I tend to write in a better way, maybe a little happier, because I get to just be with the earth and the animals on the water, maybe even a glass of whiskey in the morning with my coffee and smoking cigarettes while standing on the bow of the boat fishing butt ass naked. In my opinion, that is true nature, stark naked fishing balls blowing in the wind. I would highly recommend this to any fisherman. Just make sure you're out there early, so people don't think some deranged lunatic is flashing your genitals at fellow boaters as they pass by, but if you happen to run into this situation from either party. If you're the naked bastard on the boat, just simply wave and if you're the bystander, just think about the man and ask, what if I was in his shoes? Would you not do the same thing with balls flying, or think about what state of mind is this man in when he can enjoy the luxuries of nature and a boat like that. He must be having a good time and be in a good state of mind. Hell, maybe I'm a little unethical with it all but that, my friends, is true freedom. Just hope the passer-by in the boat doesn't call the cops because in this day in age, showing freedom in this sort of way can get you hauled straight to jail, or they just shoot the poor bastard for extrema use of freedoms. That kind of thing, my friend, is not allowed in this country anymore, you know, freedom. They just want to lock you up and throw away the key if you show your freedoms in such way. You can't let the bastards know that you are having a good time, this is not allowed in society today, even with the depressing situation that we are in. Those are the real bastards you must look out for "THE FUN POLICE, OUT TO RUIN PEOPLES HOPES AND DREAMS" and all the corruption going on today and that's why I keep up with this boat. It is one place I can go to get away from the bullshit going on. What have I done to have to deal with these people, the fun suckers and life drainers? Hopefully, someday soon, I will see and feel the love once again.

Well, it's been a few months since I left the lake new and I'm back at the lawn care business. It's fall now and the leaves are falling. This is good for me, though, because my money depends on the seasons and the trees. I clean up yards in the fall; it's not the best job or the easiest, I may add especially doing the work by yourself. It can become a daunting task at times, and luckily, I don't pay taxes doing this line of work. I'm just waiting for the day the government bastards come knocking on my door trying to get money that they didn't earn, but I hope that never happens because I only work a few days a week just to get by, so I hope the swine leave me alone. We no longer live in a time where you can grow corn and sell it. They have about twenty useless processes for selling corn that no one truly understands, and the bastards will practically bankrupt the local farmer if you attempt to your own business nickel and dime you to death. They tax the corn, the seed to plant it, the dirt you grow it in, and the water you use to grow it, even the air your breath while doing the work. Keeping you worn out and tired, making only pennies on the dollar till you're forced to sell out to these government bastards, they try to leave you no choice but to sell out. I have great respect for the independent farmer these days, I don't know how they do it, but God takes care of you all and doesn't sell out to the swine. That's why I just try to run my business under the radar as much as possible, but tier radar is getting very sophisticated these days. It's getting harder and harder to live undetected these days, the freedom taken away more and more around every corner and they are dumbing us down to the point that your average bear isn't even smart enough to see it. Or they are all just too scared to try and fight to get their freedom back.

"IF I DIE, DON'T BURY ME AT ALL. JUST PICKLE MY BONES IN ALCOHOL. PUT A BOTTLE AT MY FEET AND HEAD, IF I DON'T DRINK YOU'LL KNOW I'M DEAD"

7

BLOWING THE ENGINE ON THE 1953 ROADMASTER

T he summer was finally over, I had fought the boat and the weather if I could. It was finally too cold to stay out on the boat. I had to pull it out of the lake and winterize it. It was almost October at that time, a beautiful time to be out at the lake to see the changing colors of the trees on the lake. No more boat traffic, just peace and serenity. The season was over, it had been a month or so since I had left the lake life. It was going to be slow at that time, nothing too exciting, just fading dreams of the fun that I had at the lake. I tend to drink a little more this time of year, I think it's the weather or at least that is my excuse. I had met this girl at lunch, when I was working, she was bartending where I decided to stop and eat. I had met her there before and we got to talking she told me that I should go to fox and hound for the Tuesday night special. I really liked the place. It's a newer bar, but when they built it, the designers had good taste. The way I decide whether I like a bar is the bar itself. Fox and hounds bars are horseshoe-shaped and it is built nicely in oak. The shelves that hold the alcohol are well built, with mirrors behind the bottles. Every time I have been there, I was always greeted by a beautiful bartender and the "funguses" are very good. I met up with the girl from the bar and we shared a few drinks. We began to play pool and a couple of hours had passed; she was getting very drunk and decided she needed to leave. I decided, what the hell, I'm going to stay a little longer to see if I could cause a little ruckus before the night's end. The bartender that night was one of my favorites. Her name is Taylor; she's a stunning brunette, tall and slender with a nice behind. She tends the bar with great energy making sure that my glass is always full. I sat at the bar talking to her like I usually do when I go there. She seems to just hang around me even though she is working. I flirt with her slightly and she seems to enjoy it as I make her blush every now and again. She knows that I can drink a lot and still maintain my composure and she keeps me well taken care of, knowing that at the end of the night, I will take care of her with the tip. I always wanted to take her out but never have, she would be an absolute firecracker, I'm sure. After having about ten or so beers, I decided I should go. I had driven my 1953 Buick Roadmaster that night and I hadn't found the excitement that I was looking for that night. I climbed in the seat of the 53 and fired the car up. It started with ease despite the temperature being around 30 degrees. I sat and smoked a cigarette, letting the old car warm up. I pondered whether to go to a bar in Missouri since the last call was an hour later than Kansas. If you leave Kansas at last call, you can make it to Missouri in time for one or two more drinks.

I put the car into gear and drove towards the highway. Once I hit the highway, I hit the gas and took the car slowly to 75 mph cruising smoothly. Then suddenly, my foot smashed the floor and I had the edge to drive. I wanted to take the car for a short drive around the city, maybe a thirty-mile trip altogether. I floored the car smashing the pedal down as far as it would go, and the car started spinning the speedo up seventy-five, eighty-five, ninety-five, one hundred and five, slowly getting the car to its top speed of one hundred and ten miles per hour. I kept the pedal smashed to the floor, this was no longer a joyride. I was after the excitement I was craving that night. I mashed the pedal harder. I thought that I would push my foot right through the floorboard. The engine was screaming and burning down the road. I thought the wheels were going to fly off, the lines in the road slowly fading into on solid line from pure speed. The lights on the dash were shining bright because the engine was turning the alternator so fast it was putting out max voltage. I felt like I was a WW2 bomber flying to my target. I called the car the bomber because of the hood ornament, it was called a bomber sight, it resembled one perfectly with a circle and a V in the center. I felt like the Enola gay carrying the atomic bomb at a blazing speed, the huge metal car flying at one hundred and ten miles an hour on a path of pure destruction if a car was to pull out in front of me. I was sailing so fast as if I was flying through space. All the cars around me had turned to stars flying by at great speeds. I came to the first exit, not lifting off the throttle one bit. The car dug into the corner with ease and maintained my speed. I had to hold on tight, White knuckling the steering wheel to keep myself from flying across the bench seat since the car had no seatbelts. You would think the speed in the corner would slow me down, but it made me push harder and harder, fighting between life and death. I was in the grasp of death's hand with one false maneuver of the car, but I had to pull through.

I had done about ten miles so far, keeping my speed up the whole way. I had Kansas City in my sights now and I was coming in low and fast just looking for the cops. There was no stopping me, even if they pulled behind me, my foot was stuck to the floor with what felt like glue. I was coming into my next curve, heading westbound onto I70. Heading into dangerous curves with sinful eyes, the tires began whaling as I hit the on-ramp. The engine had to have been glowing red and spitting fire like a dragon still pegging out the speedometer. I was shocked that I didn't spin the needle right off the thing. I knew I had two sharper curves coming up very soon, with signs signalling trucks to slow down through the curves. I was testing the car's full potential as I approached the curves. The lights on the speed limits signs were flashing, warning me of potential danger, but I kept my foot dug in hard to the floor. The tires screeched around each turn this time, just barely holding enough traction to keep the car on the road. It was a sharp right turn with an immediate left. The speed limit posted was fifty miles an hour and I maintained the hundred-plus all the way through both curves. There was a car in the second curve and I passed by them like a bullet from a gun. He would have had barely enough time to realize what had happened as I flew by.

I was in the heart of the city now, the glow of the street lightsflickering through the windows like a strobe light at a disco, flashing faster and faster as I got deeper into the main nerve of the city where the highway passes under the city in a sort of tunnel. The lighting was golden in color and it lit up the whole cab of the car like a summer's day. There was one sharper curve at the end of the tunnel, which forced me to let up slightly on the accelerator pedal. I had about ten miles left till I was back at home. I was shocked that the car was maintaining so well, the temperature and oil pressure looked fine, so I mashed her back to the floor. I was shocked that I hadn't run into any police officers during the whole fiasco. Seeing the car at that sort of speed must have been a great sight to see

I was nearing the last couple of miles of the trip; everything had been smooth going till I was about a mile from my house. When suddenly, there was a bad bang deep in the motor and a severe power loss. The engine was knocking and throbbing now, making a god-awful racket. I was only about a half mile from the house. I entered the exit ramp from the highway and pulled up to the light. When I came to a stop, the engine died out, I reached down to hit the starter button, and nothing happened. I tried again and once more, nothing, on the final try, I gave the car some gas and it started. The car was shaking violently, it would not stay running unless I kept my foot on the gas. I took off from the light, just trying to limp the car the last few blocks to my house. The feeling of relief I had when I pulled into the house was great. Safe and sound, it was late, about three or four in the morning. I popped the hood looking for any noticeable damage and I could not find any. I checked the oil and it was full of antifreeze and at that point, I knew I had a serious problem. I wasn't going to do any more work that night because it was terribly cold out. I went in and went to bed. When I woke in the morning, I had a bad feeling about the car's condition. The morning was very brisk, but I got dressed and went outside to diagnose the problem. I started pulling the spark plugs and when I got to the last one, I thought everything was fine and that I had just blown a head gasket, but when I pulled the last one out, the plug had been smashed and the electrode end was completely flattened. At that point, I knew that there was serious damage and I would have to pull the engine to diagnose the problem completely

I started the process by taking off all the necessary pieces to pull the motor. Luckily on these old cars, it's not that hard to do. I had the radiator removed and the engine out in about half a day. I started by pulling the manifolds off, so I could remove the head on the bad cylinder. When I got the head off, I instantly noticed that the piston was completely gone. The only thing left was a connecting rod and it had scrapped a large hole in the side of the cylinder wall, Breaking the water jacket and causing the coolant to get into the oil. The piston itself had shattered into very small pieces in the bottom of the oil pan. I inspected the valves, and everything seemed to be ok except for one valve over the busted cylinder. The valve had broken off and the piston smashed it against the top of the head, exploding the piston to bits. Luckily the head wasn't too torn up, so it could be salvaged. I suspected that the engine was trashed.

I started doing some research trying to find a new one, soon to discover that the engine block, heads, and pistons were only made in 1953 and the part would be quite difficult to come by since it was Buicks first year of the v8, the years to follow they made many modifications to the engine making it that much harder to find parts for the thing. I was searching everywhere for an engine and a piston, slowly losing hope. Engines that I found were very expensive, from fifteen hundred all the way up to around five thousand. I feared I wouldn't have the money to fix the car. None of the engines I found was even in the state that I lived in. I was feeling rather down, but I only needed an engine block, not all the accessories, so I hoped I could find a block. Still, with no luck finding a new engine, I took mine to a machine shop to see what they had to say. I had little hope

I had made a call on an engine block up near Chicago. I thought I had found one finally; I talked to the man about coming to get it. We talked for a couple of days making sure it was infecting the right block. We verified that it was the right one and I had to arrange plans to drive to Chicago to pick it up. For some reason, I could not get ahold of the guy for a few days. When I called, it was as if his phone had been turned off. Again, I lost hope of getting the car back on the road. I eventually heard back from the machine shop and they told me to bring it in to see what they could do with the block. I stripped the engine down and brought it to them. It looked bad, but I told the old boys that I didn't have a lot of money, but I needed to get the engine fixed. He told me that he could fix the engine and it would cost around four hundred dollars for the repairs. I told them about the engine that I found, and he suggested buying it and I told him that I could no longer get ahold of the man, so I left the engine with them at the shop.

A few days later, I got a call from the guy with the engine and we set a time for me to come pick it up. I had just acquired a newer 1983 Buick Park Avenue. It is a nice car with a hundred thousand miles on the body with a new engine put in six thousand miles ago. I had only had the car for a few days after deciding to make the trip to Chicago. I went and bought a trailer hitch for the car, so I could pull a small trailer that I had borrowed from my neighbor to put the engine on. I put the trailer on and hit the road, making it for about an hour before I needed to stop for gas, smokes and a six-pack of tall boys for good measure, a wise choice for a long trip. I always suggest highway beers for highway speed straight-line driving.

I always love hopping in a new car and see if it will make the trip. I had good faith in the car and slammed two beers one after another in about ten minutes flat; feeling rather buzzed and satisfied, I smoked three cigarettes in a row keeping the car at about eighty-five miles per hour. I had never really had a car with cruise control, so I played with the new function for about an hour. I found I really didn't like the feature because when I hit a hill, it would floor itself, just draining the fuel. I have a lot better control when I use my foot because I can prepare the engine for the hill before I reach it. Instead of hitting the hill and going from eighty-five to about sixty-five before, the cruise control decides to kick in hard to try and catch back up, causing the car to nearly redline to get back up to speed.

I had been to Chicago before but had never driven up there. It was a boring trip and it took much longer than I expected to reach my destination. I originally told the man that I would be there around eight or nine o'clock. He seemed to be getting a little frustrated about my tardiness. I explained to him that I had traveled from Kansas City about seven hundred miles. My GPS. was also on the frits, so I had to navigate the old school way and not too many people know how to do this anymore. I must say I'm not the best at it but far better than most. I informed the man that I had taken a wrong turn in Albuquerque and he laughed and understood. The last few hours of the trip were god awful it was a mixed-up panicked ride to the finish. Hoping the man wouldn't fall asleep by the time I reached his shop. I pulled in around eleven o'clock at night, apologizing for the delay. He really didn't seem to mind.

He was a Buick man for sure as he wanted to check out the 83 Buick Park Avenue. So, I showed it to him he complimented how good the condition of the thing was. I opened the passenger door to give him a look at the interior and he saw all the beer cans on the passenger floorboard, he chuckled and that was the ice breaker. He immediately asked me if I wanted a beer and I told him I sure did!!! He went to the fridge in the shop and brought me one out and asked if I wanted to see the engine. I was hoping it was in better condition, but since I drove so far, there was no way that I was leaving without it. He helped me load the thing on the trailer and offered me another beer. I couldn't turn the man down on the offer. Then he asked if I wanted to look around, he had quite a few cars on the property that he showed me. It was his dad's shop and it looked like it must have been a successful auto shop at one time. His dad had kept everything, he had a separate shop full of miscellaneous parts off cars from the forties all the way to the seventies. All the parts were quite organized. I took a good part of an hour rummaging through the barn finding all sorts of treasures. I tried to buy a few miscellaneous parts from him, but the prices were too high, so we couldn't make a deal on anything

The New American Dream

except an emblem of some car that said courtesy. He had quite a few cars in the old showroom of the shop but mostly cameos that I couldn't figure out why he kept. There wasn't anything very special in there except one car in the window of the showroom. It was a sixty-something Buick convertible, all white with a black top. It was a completely original car covered with dust and in need of a thorough car wash and detailing. I didn't want to show him my true interest in the car, but he came out and said a price I damn near choked when he told me, and I immediately walked away. I started looking behind the counter on the shelves and I noticed some of his dad's racing trophies. I asked him if he would like to sell one, I had already known the answer but asked anyway, it made me sad looking at the place because it had been quite a shop, but after his father's death, the whole place went downhill rapidly. His son didn't have the knowledge or the care to keep the business afloat and he ran it to the ground, leaving nothing but a mess. We sat and talked a little while and he threw out a price for the whole place. It seemed reasonable, but the deal-breaker to me was the white Buick I liked so much. He said that didn't come with the place, but everything else did. There were three shops and a house on the property. It was about thirty miles outside of Chicago, So in a pretty good location. It would be a good investment for someone like me because I knew what just about everything was. It would be a lot of work to fix the main shop, mainly the holes in the roof, but it was well equipped with a car lift and an engine hoist. It had everything I would need to open a shop, I could picture the place looking very nice. He told me a price of one hundred and twenty thousand for the place, again though I wouldn't take the deal if the car wasn't included in the deal.

It was now about one in the morning and I needed to head out. He gave me one more beer for the road, telling me that I might need it to be able to drive through the night. I would be back in Kansas City by morning if I could maintain focus. I had made it about an hour before I started dosing off behind the wheel. I decided to pull over and get some rest and some coffee, but even with some rest and some coffee, I was still completely exhausted. I thought maybe another few beers might help me push through, but I finally just decided to get a hotel room for the night. I found the cheapest hotel room in town and took it. I think it was a motel 6. I was a little worried about the room, but I was surprisingly pleased with the room, it seemed like they just remodeled the place, so I felt very fortunate. All I brought in was myself and my typewriter containing very important documents top-secret government files. As I got to my room, I instantly crashed on the bed and fell right asleep.

The next morning, I woke up feeling refreshed. I was told that they would be serving breakfast. I walked in their dining room and took one look at what they described as food on the counter. "HOLY HELL" I thought they expected me to eat this garbage!!! I pictured myself wiping everything off the counter onto the floor, shouting that the food was poison and not even suitable for the dogs, possibly even something along the line of god sending me on a mission just to destroy this shitty breakfast so no man should have to feast from it. It would have been quite enjoyable, but the room was barren. I snapped out of my illusion and grabbed a cup of coffee and walked out the door. As I got to the car everything was in order nobody had stolen my engine!! Not that I thought anyone would. I took a sip of the coffee once I sat down in the car and immediately dumped it out the window, cursing the hotel for telling me that they served breakfast. When all it was muck and brown water. I put the car into gear and immediately pointed the car at the nearest gas station to fill the car and grab some more smokes. I then went across the street to the McDonalds to get breakfast, I ordered a sausage and egg biscuit and a coffee to help wake me up, but it was so goddamn hot that I couldn't drink it. I looked in the floorboard and there I spied a tall boy leftover from the previous day. This was the fuel that I needed. I drank the beer down quickly; it was still cold from the night spent in the car, so it went down quite smooth. I had the Buick back at eighty-five, steadily cruising home once again, burning miles one at a time.

I got about half way home when I started to notice some weather developing ahead of me. I mashed the pedal down. Suddenly running down, a dream came onto the radio. It was if the song was speaking to me, singing "I was running down a dream working on a mystery going where ever it leads, I'm running down a dream. Then the next verse came on as I was getting closer to the rain it sang" when I rolled up the sky grew dark, I put the pedal down, to make good time and picking up whatever is mine." I really felt like I was working on a mystery, I was just out following my heart and going where ever the universe took me. Deciding which way I want to choose and so far, my heart has led me on a good path. The universe has given me great gifts along the way. I mean, hell, I did just find an engine for my car for a couple of hundred bucks, a one in a million find and got a fun car trip out of the ordeal as well.

I made it back home. The trip was a great success. I unloaded the trailer and put my engine on a stand and really started to examine the thing. The engine was allotting worse condition than I thought since it had been sitting for so long in the weather, but it had the parts that I needed to get it back on the road. It took me a whole week of soaking the engine in oil and a lot of hard work to finally free up the engine. I lucked out and it had a lot more good parts in it than I thought. I managed to get a new set of pushrods and all the pistons out, which I would later find out that all the pistons were trashed. The crankshaft in the car was in a lot better shape too. As soon as I can get my engine back from the shop, I should be in good shape other than having to buy new gaskets, pistons, and valves to prevent the problem from happening again. Now it's just a waiting game to get my engine back.

8

EARLY MORNING SHOOTING

I t was the first day back in Colorado; we arrived in the early hours of the morning, too early to even think about sleep at this time. I asked my brother and mother what they had planned for the day and my mom said, we are just going to rest today. "**God almighty**" I thought I just came a thousand miles to sit around a house all day. "**Hell**" I thought, there must be something we can do on this day. With lack of sleep, I felt it was necessary to use a little St. Brendan's in my coffee. "**It was a morning for a strong drink**" in times of lack of sleep, booze always helps me out, so I had a few cups reasonably spiked. I sat and thought about the day; my mother had brought a few guns with her for what reason I don't know, but that gave me an idea she had a very nice 20-gauge shotgun and an old 4 10, so I poured myself a jack on the rocks filling the glass rather full. I asked my brother if he wanted to go shooting. It was about nine or ten in the morning. What better way to start the morning than guns? I and my brother gathered the guns and went down to the local sporting goods store in Cedaredge, Colorado. It is a very nice store but very small. We hoped we could pick up the supplies that we needed, just skeet and shells. I used to live in this town, so I knew a spot to go shoot at. I had found the place while riding my motorcycle.

It was in the adobes close to town adobes are kind of like sand dunes but harder material. I remembered a place with broken TVs that had been shot up and all sorts of other things that had been shot. We walked into the sporting goods store, hoping to get what we needed for the day. We had gotten lucky they had four boxes of 20-gauge shells and two boxes of four ten, so we bought them out of ammo and bought a box of clays. The lady working seemed rather pleased as we were checking out. A woman walked in as we were checking out, trying to sell a handgun and she asked the woman working if she knew of anyone interested. I asked her the type of gun, it ended up just being a small 22 pistol, so I told her that I wasn't interested so I paid the owner of the shop and walked out. She seemed very pleased with the cash I gave her, almost like she hadn't seen cash in ages. People don't know what to do with cash these days, it's all fucking credit cards. The lady thanked me and told me and my brother not to have too much fun the rest of the day with a smile on her face. I asked her about the place to shoot and she confirmed the place talking about the TVs that were shot to hell. She managed to give us very good directions to the spot and off we went. We passed a cop right before we got to the shooting range and I turned to my brother and said. "LOOK, THEY ARE ON TO US ALREADY AND WE HAVENT EVEN DONE ANYTHING" We are just a couple of brothers out to have a good time with guns. This in fact, is the American dream at its finest, and the coppers are already out to get us. Luckily the cop kept on driving and we arrived at the spot. The first few shots rang out like angels calling us from heaven. This, my brother, is what vacation is all about, I said, and he agreed. We started off with the clay pigeons and the 20 gauge we were both on point with the gun, so we decided to get the 4 10 out and gave that a try. A 4 10 takes great skill to shoot and it took us both a few shots before we got comfortable with the gun. There's just something about shooting that early in the morn-ing. We decided to make it a little more interesting and we started to shoot the little bits of glass bottlenecks leftover from a previous enthusiast. Then we started shooting our spent shells, that's the true skill. It takes a lot to hold the shell in one hand and gun in the other and toss the shell up to yourself while having to shoulder your gun and blast the small shell out of the sky. We even started shooting the little 4 10 shells. We were well warmed up at that point, our eyes were on point now. We were running out of clays and we had to get creative with the rest of the shells. I had my brother throw up a tin can. I had three shells in the gun and I managed to hit the can with every shot before it hit the ground, so I told my brother to give it a go and he matched the shots after two tries. Good shooting, I told him, at that point, I found a tire laying on the ground and I picked it up and started walking up the nearest hill to roll it down. I told him that this was a hog simulation and to pretend the beast was charging down the hill at him. Now I have never had the opportunity to shoot a hog, but the tire seemed about the right size. I wanted to roll one down the hill right at him, so maybe he could experience the fear of a hog running full force at him. I rolled the tire down the hill and it began picking up speed rapidly. There wasn't as much thrill as I thought because the 20-gauge shells didn't even phase the thing. I figured it would have at least knocked the thing over, but nothing. Damn, I thought. My brother was making his way up the hill and he found one last shell in his pocket, giving me the last shot of the morning. That's the cool thing about my younger brother is that he just wants to have fun just like myself, who cares who has the last shot, but for some reason, he thought to give me the last one.

It was a muddy mess out there and we had my mom's new car, so we had to figure out how to get into the car without getting the muck all over the inside. My brother took his boots off and it was rather amusing watching him climb through the back of the car over both rows of seats to get into the driver's seat. Now it was my turn and I couldn't take my boots off and walk around to the passenger seat, so I walked out to the road where I could walk in my socks around the car to get in. I had my back turned to my brother as he drove up behind me to meet me on the road, but when I turned around, I saw that my brother had missed the bridge over the ditch and had managed to get the front right tire of the car in the ditch.

When I looked at the thing, it was a funny sight. The car was only on two wheels cattycorner to each other and was rocking back and forth on the two as he tried to reverse out of the predicament. It was funny to watch and both of us hoped we didn't mess up my mom's new Subaru. He couldn't get out of there, but luckily, the car was well balanced between the two tires and I was able to lift the car to get a third wheel down on the ground and he backed out with no problem. As we were leaving, we both agreed that the little car was a very rugged machine. We had also made an agreement not to tell my mother to put her car into the ditch. But we had done a thorough off-road test with her car, so we now felt comfortable with her driving the car. When we got back to the house, the first thing I said to my mom was that her car had great off reading capabilities, my brother and I laughed, and my mother had no idea what we were talking about, but that was the fun of it all. We had an inside joke the rest of the trip and my mother will never know till she reads this someday. She honestly shouldn't care since the car wasn't damaged in the ordeal.

My brother and I then decided that we must go in search of some fine Colorado medical marijuana, but the nearest place was a two-hour drive away but only thirty minutes from Ouray, Colorado, one of my favorite towns on the western slope. We pulled into the pot shops parking lot, both in muddy as fuck boots, so I decided to take my boots off outside and walk in barefoot. I wasn't too sure what they would sometimes say, these kinds of things throw people off. We managed to accomplish the mission without any major problems hell the two hippie women behind the counter were probably barefoot themselves , but I had forgotten to check and see, but a stressful job like selling the devil's lettuce, you must need some serious grounding to cope with the animals and lunatics walking in with no shoes in the dead of winter must be terribly stressful. Who knows though, they are probably used to that kind of thing. We had managed to get out of the place unsaved, so I went to the gas station next door to get some rolling papers. I figured a joint was the best option at that time. We got back in the car and proceeded to Ouray. I told my brother that would be the best place for a joint and he took my word for it. We also had a flask and a case of beer with us for good measure. We had almost finished the beer by the time we got there. We stopped on the side of the road right before we reached the red mountain pass; we looked back over the town as I sparked up the joint. It was a marvelous site to sit there and look over Ouray, it's a great town. Whoever decided to build a town in this spot must have been off their rocker a little because the town is surrounded by sheer cliffs on every side. The town is only about a dozen square blocks around, but it is a truly beautiful place. The snow was falling and very thick this time of year. It was a very relaxing spot to sit and smoke the joint. I looked next to the car where I had found a road cone and proceeded to pick it up and yell through the thing like a huge microphone. We just had to let the whole town know that the McAuley brothers had shown up. We had wondered if the town's people could hear us. There was a pretty good echo through the canyon, so I'm sure that they could. We finished off the joint and I finished my beer. I then put the road cone on my head like a giant orange dunce cap and again began to yell, telling the town to "**WATCH OUT**" I bet anyone watching this obscene site would have been very leery of getting anywhere near us. My brother decided to take a picture for photographic evidence of the whole ordeal. The cone then fell over my face and I bent over and stuck my new pointed head straight into the snowplow mound right next to me like an ostrich does when they are startled. My brother then took one more picture. We decided to go after that before someone might decide to call the cops, but we couldn't leave until one of us could get the cone stuck on top of a road sign next to where we were parked. We had to leave our mark somehow to let the town folks know that someone had managed to have fun at that very spot. My brother thought that we should have stolen the road cone and taken it snowboarding the next day to wear it down the mountain the next day. I told him that it was a bad idea to keep such evidence of the Haines crimes we had committed while sitting mountainside smoking a joint. When we left, though, I knew he was right, we should have taken a souvenir. The car ride back to cedar edge was nice since we were still toasted and slightly buzzed. I still had a little Jack Daniels in my flask, so we had enough booze to tide us over until we got home. Hell, it felt like it took an eternity to get there, but since we were highly medicated on the way back, it was like we were never even in the car. It felt like a damn time warp all the way back faster than the speed of sound. Not through just good conversations and tunes got us back lackaday split. It turned out to be a pretty good day considering everyone just wanted to rest, I was glad I decided to get my brother out and about because the day turned out quite good.

9

GOD TALK AND THE GREAT SPIRIT

So, my brother and I had had a great time out in the mountains, causing a ruckus. My mother and this man are complete God freaks. They are a rare sort so obsessed with the fact that they love God that they don't really understand how uncomfortable they can make people feel. Especially ones like me and my brother who just spent the whole day shooting, drinking, and smoking the devil's lettuce, a day of great activities in our eyes, but the last thing anyone wants after a day like this is to be preached on with the word of the Lord. Now I'm not one to criticize, but there's one thing about me, that I do not try to force my religion on others. Hell, most people would find my views insane but fuck it, everyone has the right to believe their own things. But there is one thing that drives me off my rocker and that is getting preached on by bible thumpers. The funny thing about these people is if you believe anything other than Jesus and God, you are in fact the devil!!! And they will try and save you. If you don't want to hear what they say, they in fact turn into the devil they despise. It's funny how people of religion have so many demons within them; well, I guess that's why they go to church so much. I myself find my religion in love, nature, guns, alcohol, pot and good music, but God forbid this kind of blas-

phemy in the Christian fate. If you are not one of them, they will try
their dandiest to try to convert you. Hell, they're almost as bad as the
Jahvist witnesses, but at least they don't go knocking on your door.
We had some Jahvist witnesses come by one time and my mother let
them in down on their religion. They were two younger guys, maybe
in their twenties. I left the room to let my mother talk with them. I
went to my room to rip fat bowls out of my bong; the room wasn't far
off the living room and I'm sure they heard the gurgling in the bong
and smelt the pot. When I went back into the living room, they were
both sitting there looking like puppy dogs begging for bong rips, so I
guess they're not so bad. Now when these bible thumpers get the
chance to try and convert someone, they pounce on them like wolves
on a sheep. I don't know if they can see themselves acting in this way,
but it is one of the most unholy things that I have ever experienced.
Hell, no one is that happy all the time, there is bad in the world as
well and it's a fine balance like the yin and the yang. If you are happy
all the time, in fact, you will never really know what true happiness
really is; you must experience some lows to experience some highs.
These god-fearing people act so innocent and perfect, they come off
as phony because no one is that happy. They are like time bombs
waiting to go off because they don't know how to deal with their
problems. The church isn't helping them much, it is a false sense of
security for them. If I was to start a church, it would be at 5oclock just
in time for happy hour and it would be a place where everyone is
welcome and there would be good food and spirits for all, maybe
some bluegrass and other sorts of live music. It would be a social
gathering or town meeting a time for folks to network with each
other and converse and ask how everyone is doing. Hell, maybe it
even has a bonfire that people could sit around. Back to the main
point though, some of these Christians are like vultures flying circles
in the air, waiting for their next dead carcass to try and devour. Especially if you are someone like me, the Christians talk a good story, but
in the end, if you are to ask them for help, they will be the first ones to
throw you to the curb and stomp your teeth in. Or even worse, they
will put you up on a fucking cross somewhere. God forbid speaking

your own opinion to these people. That's what angers them the most if you make them think for a second that maybe their beliefs could be complete bullshit, but so maybe my own, but I still give them a chance to express their own opinions but won't open an ear to anything else. My first argument is that there were civilizations for thousands of years before there was a Jesus and a bible and what did these people believe in??? That fact alone makes me question the whole thing.

my brother and I came back from the house after a day of blasphemy and hellraising to get preached on by my new stepdad the all-holy Kevin, but as I sat and ate dinner and discussed the topic of religion. He was, in fact, trying to push my buttons but I, not being affected by his attempts, was in fact pushing his own. Now, this is a godly man I'm talking about, do not forget that. As he was preaching to me as I was trying to enjoy my dinner, he was clenching his fists in rage as I listened to his sermon. Hell, that was one of the scariest things I think I have ever seen. A holy man, gritting his teeth and white-knuckling while preaching the "WORD OF THE LORD" "JESUS CHRIST" I thought if Jesus saw this man acting in this manner he would slap him alongside the head with the bible himself and ask him what he had really learned from it.

I began telling him some of my beliefs about the yin and the yang and the Great Spirit or Gaia, the planet on which we live and how my beliefs I had gathered mostly from looking at the earth and seeing how it functions. When you take care of the earth, it will take care of you. He didn't want to hear anything of the sort, but hell, if it wasn't for the earth, there would have never been a Jesus or anything, as a matter of fact. Now I try to be a peaceful man, but I mentioned the yin and the yang and my mother herself said, who cares about that Chinese bullshit. For her to say, that makes me say the same about the Christian fate. You know, maybe it is bullshit, but at least I have the balls to admit that I may be wrong, how can you be wrong on a subject that there is no answer to??? I also have the balls to admit that every man and woman has a dark and a light side to them and that society wants to get rid of the dark altogether, but there are primitive instincts in men that people hide away. This is not good, I myself let these feelings out with guns, explosions, and hunting. Now hunting that's a religion all in itself, every man has a hunting instinct in them, it's the same as a lion after a water buffalo or a hawk after a rabbit, it's the urge to kill or a taste for blood. Hunting is wild in this way and once you let it get in your blood, it never goes away. As they say "THAT DOG WILL HUNT" it's in us all, but society has robbed us of our natural instincts. I was trying to explain this to Kevin and he told me it was bullshit, but as I watched his white knuckles, I could tell that he had it in him and he had held it back for so long he was about to jump across the table and try and strangle me the true beast was coming alive in him and it was Jesus who was bringing it out in him. Now me and my brother went out that morning to let this rage out by shooting, so we were nice and calm. We had asked him to go with us, but he did not. He really needed to though church just wasn't doing it for him. He didn't understand what I was saying, but he was the perfect example sitting right in front of me. He just didn't understand. He must have been deprived as a child. The funny thing is that I know Christians that hunt, for example, the duck dynasty family. They formed their life around hunting and they go to church to ask for forgiveness and that's the yin and yang at its finest. Where I myself am in church as I am hunting and that is Mother Nature herself, she will provide an animal for you to take that is the beauty of it all. Is that Mother Nature is the strongest and I get protection from her and the beings on her to keep things right because she knows that people are getting it all messed up anymore. So at least I have that going for me. The trees, the birds and the animals can protect me far better than anything else because if you are on their side, they will defiantly be on yours. People themselves are the true beasts, they are all mad, well, not all of them, but I prefer to be an animal, not a beast. If only animals could talk, oh how people would shut up very fast. "FOOLS" is what people are anymore and they try to bring you down, but really, they just bring themselves to their own doom and demise, they have been doing it for years. "FUCK IT THOUGH" let them bring themselves down, I can keep myself entertained watching the real beasts in the zoo. The truth of the matter is that the beasts are already in the zoo and kept in their cages, they are not much fun to watch anymore because they are all just pinned up and rotting away slowly, but they can't even see that they are all walking skeletons. Who's the one laughing then once they realized that? I myself feel like one of the few still living in the world, or at least I try to live. I'm not happy with the world, so I create my own and live my own way, but I always look up even when the beasts are nipping at my heels, but I just kick them off as if they were small annoying dogs. Hell, though I was trying to help my stepdad out by telling him to hunt to let out his frustration, but instead, the word of the Lord rushed through him like some sort of beast trying to escape his fake body. It was sad in a way to see a man like this because he didn't know how to handle the situation. If he had just gone shooting with me and my brother, he would have been allotting better off. It would have done him a lot of good to let some of that aggression out, but hell, that's why I'm not a preacher because who likes guns and drinking a little booze? No one would show up to my church "HAHA" Keep the word of the lord out of my church because if you let it in, the true beasts will show themselves. I myself just want to see good in people having a good time, that's why I like the idea of my kind of church. What do you think the savior Jesus Christ would think if he showed up to a party for church service? He would pull up just in time for happy hour and would be thrilled because the Jesus I believe in was an outlaw. That's why he caused a ruckus everywhere he went? He was a mold-breaker trying to make things better for the people, but what did they do? They hung the man upon a goddamn cross. I always figured if Jesus was to return like the bible said he would, he would most defiantly bring his attorney to lock all the bastards up for good this time. He died for all of them once and what did they do? They went and fucked it all up a lot more they didn't keep fighting for what he gave his life for. They just went back to bowing down to the bullshit man. So, he indeed would not give his life for the people again "THAT'S FOR DAMN SURE" why would he.

I managed to finish dinner and not get my head torn off by the beast. I was glad my brother was there to back me up at the table. "SCARY STUFF THOSE BIBLE THUMPERS" After dinner, I stepped outside and smoked a good bowl of pot and poured myself a drink. Luckily, we had a day of snowboarding planned for the following day.

10

THE EYES OF A CHILD

We woke up the following day and had skiing on our minds; my brother and I started off with coffee and a little booze in each cup that we had. My mom checked the weather that morning to find out that the top of the mountain had gotten quite a bit of snow the night before and it was snowing that morning. We didn't know if we could make it to the top of the mountain to ski, but we decided to try anyway. When we left, the roads were pretty good for the first ten miles or so, but the road worsened as we climbed in elevation. The mountain road had a barrier to keep you from going up the road if conditions were too bad, but the gate was open. My brother was driving the car and my mother was getting nervous about the conditions. They were getting worse and the bumper of the car was plowing through the deep snow and it was flying up over the hood. We were forced to keep the windshield wipers on the whole time because the snow would come crashing over the hood like rough seas over the bow of a boat. My brother and I were determined to make it, even though my mom was nervous, she still stayed on board. We came to a corner where an oncoming truck was heading our way. We had to cut over sharp just to get out of the man's way, almost pushing us off the road; it was a heart-stopping moment, but we maintained. As we reached the top of the mountain, we had our stresses relieved, knowing that we were getting closer to our destination. Luckily at the top of the mountain, the sky had cleared, and we could finally see the sun. We knew it was going to be a good day at that point. There were some great views from the top of the mountain. The lakes up there were frozen, but they were a beautiful sight to see. We worked our way down the backside of the mountain and the resort came into sight. When we arrived, there were cars lined up clear down the road into the parking lot. We thought about grabbing the first one that we saw, but we decided to take a chance and drive to the parking lot, hoping to get a spot. To our surprise, we got one not too far from the main lift. I had filled my flask before we left, so my brother and I took a pull from it before walking in to buy our lift tickets. I had forgotten my sunglasses and needed some for the mountain and my brother wanted to buy some goggles. We walked into the shop as my mother bought us our lift tickets, all my brother wanted was some goggles, but the cheapest pair was around 75 dollars, "god awful" I thought I was looking for just a normal pair of aviators. I managed to find a pair, but they ended up being child size, but they fit my face pretty well. I went to check out as my brother kept searching for a pair. The lady at the counter saw that they were kid's sunglasses and she asked me if I was sure that I wanted to buy them, telling me that I could not return them once I paid for them. I told her that this was fine. I made a remark to her that it was better to see the world through the eyes of a child anyway, so I didn't mind. She looked at me with a big smile on her face. My brother finally just bought a pair of sunglasses as well. We met back up with my mother and made our way to the lift and got on. As we made our way up, my brother pulled out his pipe and loaded it with some pot. It's cool because my mother really doesn't bust our chops too much for smoking weed. My brother passed the thing to me, but I only took one toke because I really don't smoke too much, but I did take another pull off my flask. As we approached the top of the lift, we all got a little nervous because we are from Kansas, not really mountain people. It is kind of sketchy hopping off, especially because you have everyone from the mountain behind you, so if you fall, you had better get the hell out of the way as fast as possible. Once you get to the top, though, you get a view of the whole place and surrounding areas. We made our way to a bench and my brother and me got strapped into our boards. It was a downhill battle from there, but we carved the mountain like we had been there before. We made a few different passes before deciding to stop for lunch. I myself didn't want food, I craved strong drink, so I made my way to the bar and ordered a bloody Mary. As I was ordering, a cute girl sitting to the left of me was staring at me with desire in her eyes. I made some small talk with her but probably should have sat down, but my brother and I wanted to get as many passes on the mountain as we could. We stepped outside to finish our drinks and smoke a cigarette. These Colorado people were looking at us like we were heathen, but they left us alone as my brother was standing there, a small chunk of snow fell from the roof, nearly landing on his drink, so we stepped away from the building. About 30 seconds after we stepped away, the snow on the roof had slid off and piled up on the table we sat at. We laughed and said that was lucky and right after that, they sent the crew out to break the snow from the roof. I scooped some snow into my bloody Mary for good measure and chugged the rest of it. I took my glass back inside to give to the bartender making sure that I acknowledged the girl sitting at the bar. My brother and I hopped back on the lift. We only had time for a couple more trips, so we decided to hit the triple black on the mountain. It was full of moguls and obstacles, but we both made it through pretty well me being surprised by how much fun it was throwing as many obstacles in front of me as possible. My brother didn't have any problems either, but he has been snow-boarding a few more times than me, so it was expected, but I caught on fast. After we got through there, we decided to make one last trip. We got to the top and sat down to have a break and a smoke when we decided to howl like wolfs from the top of the mountain and to my surprise, we had a guy next to us let out a howl letting us know that we were not the only hooligans out there on that day. I had to take a wee and took my board off to walk to the side of the mountain in the trees. When I got back in there and finished my wee, I started walking back towards my brother and fell through the crust of the snow in the trees, getting stuck in snow almost to my nipples. I had managed to wiggle around and tried to lie down on the snow. I basically had to roll to get out of the snow. It was a stressful situation till I figured everything out. We made our final run down the mountain and headed back to the car, all of us feeling rather worn out but satisfied with the day. Luckily the road was in a little better shape on the way back after having cars drive over it a few times before we got to it. We stopped at the liquor store when we got back in town, I normally don't drink as much as I did on this trip, but when I'm on vacation, I prefer to indulge in booze, cigarettes and occasionally other substances when available. My mom's soon to be husband looked a little nervous about the amount of booze I was consuming. He eventually saw that I could handle my liquor very well and started pouring me drinks from his favorite bottle, trying to test me to see if he could push me over the edge tonight, but I didn't give him that satisfaction. I just damn near finished his bottle and laughed. By the end of the night, he kind of offended me, telling me that my Jack Daniels was shit and his whiskey was better. Now I'll admit the whiskey he had was good and very smooth, but I like the jack because it does go down a little rough, forcing me to sip on it and take my time. I like just about all whiskeys, even the cheap stuff like Even Williams, it's cheap but it's very good over ice. Most people would never even try it like that because it is so cheap, but it's exceptionally good, in my opinion.

11

THE TRIP TO ASPEN

Well, my brother and I had finally left my mom's house. We had a long drive ahead of us to make it back to Kansas City. I had suggested that we make a trip to Aspen, Colorado, to see a girl that I knew from back when also to visit my friend Emanuel. Aspen was a little out of the way but not too far. It was a much more scenic route to go the way that we did. They were roads untraveled to both of us, lots of two-lane highways with great views the whole way. As we were driving, we passed many small towns that had damn near been deserted by society. They seemed like great places to live, in my opinion, far away from all the hustle and bustle of the city. As we drove through, we passed through town after town of what looked like ghost towns. It was eerie in a way because it looked like they were once booming towns in their heyday must have been old mining towns. But I guess when the money ran out, so did the people who fled these beautiful places leaving behind a worn out and forgotten place. It seems odd to me that people would leave such beauty for the almighty dollar. Places of serenity and relaxation. We continued to drive through town after town like this, coming towards a mountain pass, the road became much more treacherous full of steep hills and sharp curves. It was a national park for about twenty miles through the pass, all signs of human life had left the roadside just a view of nature, a truly relaxing feeling, pine and Aspen trees looking as if they were cascading down the side of the mountains. As we got to the top of the pass, we topped the hill revealing the road ahead to come. It looked to be about twenty miles long to make the distance of about a mile as the crow flies. Full of hairpin turns and steep downhill grades. As we made our way down the backside of the mountain, we started getting into some nice-looking valleys with the occasional farm with a few acres. I imagined myself having a nice piece of property like this someday. I kept thinking about how long it would take me to get money to buy a place like that. As we drove, we came to a narrow canyon where there was only enough room for a river and a road to run through, with sheer cliffs on either side of the road. Every now and again, there were small lakes where the river had pooled the water. In these parts, the water was crystal clear. I kept telling my brother that we should stop and fill all the water bottles we had in the car up. Just the sight of the water made me extremely thirsty. The next lake we came to had a bunch of dead trees surrounding the backside of the lake, where we saw a bald eagle circling a tree that had a next in it. It was February, so the lakes were still frozen except for a few parts where the water flowed. We were about an hour away from Aspen at this point, so I began to call Tori and my buddy Emanuel to get arrangements set up for my brother and me to stay the night. We were initially just stopping in for lunch and heading on our way. It took much convincing to talk my brother into staying longer because he had work in two ways. We went to where Tori worked and sat down for lunch. We sat down in her section, so we could talk to her as she worked. We sat outside next to the bottom of the ski slope. You could see all the lifts passing us by, full of skiers enjoying the mountain. It was surprisingly warm for being in such high altitudes and snow covering the ground. We had managed to get a table next to the fire pit, so it was rather nice. We hadn't sat down too long before a group of cute women came and asked if they could join us. I told them that it was just fine and that it

87

wasn't our patio to decide in a joking manner, they laughed and took a seat.

My brother and I sat with a few different groups of people. I used this chance to try and network with the locals looking for work if I decided to stay in the town. I met a lot of good people. Tori kept stopping by while my brother and I sat and drank. She got a drink from the bar that the group we were sitting with didn't order and she chugged it down very quickly to not let her boss see. She said that she really needed that drink. I was hoping I had a place to stay with her. We had made a deal previously where I lent her some money because she was in a bind. It was supposed to be in trade for a place to stay for a few days when I made it out, but when my brother and I showed up, she told me that she was living with a boyfriend of hers and that he was kind of an ass and he wouldn't want degenerates like my brother and I to stay the night. I completely understood, and the time spent there with her was fun. It was time for my brother and me to leave and I still had to convince him to stay one more night. I offered to pay for his lift ticket the next day, telling him that the price of his ticket would be the same price as my bust ticket; if I had to buy one, it would cost around 250 for the ticket, but again he said he couldn't stay because of work.

We were getting into the car when my buddy Emanuel called and told us that we should make our way to his place and he told us that there was a show that night in town. He told us that it was sold out and he didn't think we could get tickets, but I told him that we would find some there. He didn't have much hope for us, but I knew that I would get my brother and me some. My brother and I made it to Emanuel's house and he told us the door was unlocked and we were welcome to come in. It was about thirty minutes before Emanuel showed up, my brother had asked him to get him some cocaine and he found some somewhere in town. I watched as they partook in the stuff, but I didn't need that kind of thing. I'm always high-strung naturally and if I want any kind of drugs, it's some that will bring me down a level. I prefer to stick to my booze and pot with the occasional other substance. We sat and talked about going to the show. We only had a couple of hours before it began. We decided to go over to Emanuel's friend's house for a bit to smoke some of the weed that we had bought. As we sat there, I was drinking heavily and in no mood to take shit off the swine. Emanuel's friend was going out to smoke a cigarette and I offered to join him. It was rather cold outside and quite windy, so I let my smoke on the porch. He walked off into the parking lot to light his and I asked him why he would want to be out in the wind, he then very rudely barked at me to get out in the parking lot. I looked at the guy and said this is America, man, why don't you feel comfortable smoking on your own porch and this enraged the kid and he came storming to the door rushing inside to cry. The kid knew I was right, but he didn't have the balls to stand up for his rights. I finished my smoke and went to go back inside. As I opened the door, Emanuel ran to the door, telling them that the kid wanted me to leave these pussy kids like this don't do well with me. They flt threatened and the only option they can come up with is to kick me out. I laughed at the kid and waited for my brother to come out. I needed to get my bag of weed off the table and I had thought that I had left my homemade pipe on the table, which I needed as well. To my surprise, Emanuel came out the door before my brother and said yea fuck it, man let's get out here as soon as he said that, my brother came out the door. This was a door that I didn't want to open again fuck those swine, I thought to myself, I think Emanuel and my brother agreed. We left there and headed straight for the show, Emanuel again telling us that we would not find any tickets. As soon as we walked up to the venue hosting the show, there was a girl named Sarah outside the door and she looked right at me, asking if I wanted to buy some tickets. I told her hell yes and that I needed one for my brother as well. She told me the price and I think it was something around 40 or 50 bucks for the pair of them. It came out to be about the price of the one that Emanuel bought. He seemed shocked that we managed to get such a great deal. But the three of us walked in. The room was packed with beautiful women and the stage was lit up with lights. My first instinct when I walk in a place like this is to head straight to the bar. It took me a while to get up to buy a drink, but when I did, there was a very tall beauty standing right in front of me. She turned around with a smile and stepped off to the side as I ordered my drink. She was waiting for me to order and as soon as I did, I turned and looked at her beauty was out of this world. We talked for quite some time and I told her that I must find my brother and friend. I turned around to a room full of people dancing. It was something out of a 70s disco party or something. The women were dancing around in little outfits, all looking beautiful as ever. My search for my friends was cut short when the girls got in front of me. I stepped back to the bar where the taller girl was and to my surprise, she was still there, so we both leaned against the bar and watched the whole place. She was something else and I don't know why she was talking to me, but I did not mind at all. It was like a scene out of a movie watching all the people dance with a hot girl by my side. I told her that I needed to step out for a smoke and that's when the trouble began. I sat outside and smoked and went to go back inside through a door next to me; the man said that this was the V.I.P. entrance and I could not enter. There was no one else at the door and I asked what the big deal was. The other door was only about 100ft away and I asked him what the difference was. This angered the man and I shouted out something about him being a chump and lowlife; he said I was banned from the place, but I walked around the building and when the man was looking away, I snuck in the other door "FUCK THAT GUY" I thought when I was back inside I managed to find my brother telling him about the faggot door guy. My brother laughed and said we would not take any guff off these faggots. I said you're right, brother, we can't let them treat us like this those "FUCKING SWINES"

My brother and I went back to the bar and I pointed out the guard that tried to kick me out. I tried to hide a little to not let the man see me. My brother laughed at me, saying fuck that guy and I agreed with him, leaning back on the bar. I then saw the tall girl from the bar and pointed her out to my brother. I told him that she was dynamite and that he should go talk to her because she was his height and a few inches taller than me, which has never really been a problem for me but I told him to have at it. He laughed and said let's get another drink. About the time the drinks came around, the man from the door had spotted me. I said look, the bastard has me; now he came towards me and I think the presence of me with my brother the man veered off quickly. The bastard looked right at me and just turned away, thank God, I thought. About this time, Emanuel showed up again too, the band was playing their final song and we were ready to go. I got one last glance at the tall girl before leaving. She smiled at me as I walked out.

My brother and Emanuel wanted to continue to do cocaine and smoke but my drug of choice is women. Yeah, I drink like a fish and smoke pot, but that really doesn't count. There really is no better high than a good woman. I don't care what kind of drugs I take, the prospects of a good woman are overwhelming. We caught the bus back to Emanuel's and I saw another beautiful woman on the bus. She smiled at me as I hopped on board and I just went and sat right next to her. I don't know what it was, but we were drawn like magnets. I don't think we spoke more than five words before we were in some sort of make-out frenzy right there on the bus like there was nobody around. We neared the stop for Emanuel's house and the girl told me her stop was the next one. I told my brother and Emanuel that I was going to the next stop they didn't argue and hopped off. The girl and I made out some more and we got to her stop. She told me that I should have just gotten off with my brother and friend. I said what the hell connections like this are hard to come by. She told me straight forward that she wasn't going to take me back to her house, and I said ok, but I asked her if she wanted to just bullshit for a little while. She laughed and said where here on the corner I laughed and said yea this is a reasonable place. I sat down on the sidewalk and asked her to sit down. She sat next to me and we talked and looked at the stars for about thirty minutes until she said she was cold and needed to go home. She at least left me with a kiss and she was gone, saying that maybe we will see each other again.

Now at this point, I was drunk, and my phone was almost dead. I had enough battery to call my brother once to tell him that I was on my way. I now had the challenge of walking back a bus stop and finding my buddies' apartment. I hadn't spent much time in the town, but I thought that I had a good idea of where I was going. I started the walk back the skyway clear that night and I could see millions of stars. I made my way closer and made a turn, just hoping that it was the right way. My phone was completely dead by then so no idea of where I was going. Luckily, my brother and I had this code whistle that we used while hunting to find each other in the woods and as I walked, I kept whistling and as I got worried, I heard my brother whistle back. It was cool how I found my way back. It's funny how these little tricks you learn as a kid can come into play to get you back home and out of trouble. We got back to the apartment and I passed out for the night.

12

THE DROP OFF

The following morning, I tried once more to get my brother to go snowboarding, but I couldn't convince him, but I had an urge to stay in the town to keep my vacation going. I had him take me to where Tori worked and asked him to just drop me off. I was waiting for Tori to get off work. My brother was ready to get on the road and I told him that I was staying and that my work there was not yet finished. He looked at me puzzled as I started grabbing the essentials needed for my stay. I had enough cash for a few nights of hotel rooms, maybe about 700 dollars altogether. The few things I grabbed were my typewriter and a small duffle bag with a few sets of clothes. I stepped away from the car and he again asked if I was positive about my decision I really wasn't sure if I was or not, but I figured, if you're going to do something well, then you better do it right. If anything, I figured it would be a great opportunity for a good story.

There I was, standing in the middle of a parking lot with my few things in hand in Snowmass village. "WHAT NEXT" I thought I figured the best option at that point was to find the local watering hole and get a drink. I took my things and started walking, finding a nice breakfast joint in town with a bar open first thing in the morning. "PERFECT" I thought. I walked in and sat down, there was an older lady working the bar. It was still early in the morning and I craved a strong drink. I had the woman make me a bloody Mary. It was quite good. I then asked her the price of the thing was. She told me some ungodly price, I almost fell off the stool and told her that that was ridiculous. I decided to get to brass tacks with her and I told her that I was in town on a budget and that I would need plenty more booze to make it through this great ordeal. She smiled softly, telling me that there was a liquor store a few doors down and to go there if I needed more booze. I ordered breakfast and told the lady to take her time putting in my order letting her know that I had to run out for a minute. I went and bought a fifth of even Williams and came back to the breakfast joint. I walked in and sat down, putting my bottle on the bar and filling my diminishing bloody Mary clear back to the top with straight whiskey. The woman watched me do this and didn't seem to mind at all. As soon as I finished topping my drink off the women brought my food out to me. "PERFECT TIMING" I said; she smiled, asking me if I was having a rough day. I laughed and looked her straight in the eye and said no, this is an average day, but my brother had left me in the town to deal with the swine alone. She seemed completely astonished with the amount of Even Williams in the bloody Mary glass.

As I sat and drank, I texted Tori to see if she wanted to join me for breakfast. She said that she would meet me there soon; I had to ask her if she would let me stay a night. I sat and pondered where I would go if she didn't let me stay, but that really wasn't the point. I was out there looking for it, "THE AMERICAN DREAM" these kinds of trips take very little planning because it is so scarce anymore. It's like searching for bigfoot, some say it's out there, but most people think it is just a hoax. But I myself have found it a few times and it was never when I was looking for it. It was always with wild bursts of madness and filigree.

The lady served me my breakfast. I looked down at it and it was a terrible sight, the eggs were dry, and the bacon overcooked. The sight of the breakfast made me sick I looked back up at my drink and it seemed like a far better option. At that point, an older man came and sat down next to me. I could feel him looking me over as if I was a mad man, which he wasn't too far off from the truth at that point. I asked the man if he wanted a drink since I had a whole bottle sitting on the bar. I told him that I had tried to buy a whole bottle from the bar, and they informed me that they could not sell it to me. The man seemed disgusted with me and as soon as he got his meal, he picked up his whole plate and got up and walked away to go sit somewhere else. "FUCK THE MAN" I thought as I sat there pondering about my life and what to do next. I texted Tori to see where she was she said that she would be there shortly. "HELL, YES, I THOUGHT" I sat there twirling my eggs on the plate, not interested at all in eating them. I heard the doorbell ring, so I spun around on my stool and in walked two police officers. The man had called the cops. "FUCK" I thought I was just there, minding my own business, not causing any problems. I paid for my meal and they escorted me out of the restaurant. They really didn't have much to say; they asked to have my bottle and I told them that it was, in fact, my property and I would not give it up. About that time, Tori showed up at perfect timing, I thought, till she kind of yelled at me, telling me to just give them my bottle. She reached into my bag and handed it to them. They then said that I had to come with them to the police station. Once there, I was inspected, neglected and detected. After about fifteen minutes of sitting there, I asked them if I could leave in a joking manner and to my surprise, they looked at me and said "OK" They handed me a ticket or something. I didn't even look at the thing, I just took it and crumbled it up and stuffed it in my pocket. I hope it wasn't important because shortly after, it was misplaced. As I was leaving the station, I asked for my typewriter and things back and the bastards said that they left them in Snowmass and that I would have to go back there. I said to them "WHAT THE FUCK" I had very important documents in there and that I needed them back right away. As I sat on the other side of the desk, I spotted a jar with dog treats in it and as the officer was on the phone finding out where my stuff was, I reached into the jar and pulled out the dog treat and took a big bite out of the thing, the officer was stunned as I slowly ate the rest of it. As he finished up his phone call, he hung up and I started reaching for the cookie jar again to get another treat. He snapped fiercely at me, saying that I could not have another one I said "FUCK, MAN, IF YOUR FEEDING THESE THINGS TO DOGS, I MUST SURELY BE ABLE TO HAVE ANOTHER ONE" he snapped again, saying to cut the crap, I then snapped back at him telling him that it was un-American to take my things and not have them waiting for me as I was released. I also told them that they were wasting my time. He then told me that the town had a free bus that I could hop on to get back to my belongings. I walked out of doors free once more and caught the first bus back to Snowmass to retrieve my things. I had managed to get a room in Aspen for the night and to reflect on the day's experiences and relax. I had a few stiff drinks and decided to go out on the town. I made my way to an old hotel in the town. It was a rustic place, probably the oldest hotel in town, the Jerome. The rooms in the place were some-where around 1000 dollars a night. Surprisingly the drinks at the bar were reasonable, though. As I sat enjoying the antique bar made of rich wood and designed in the early 1900s, a truly beautiful sight to see. It's something you don't get much these days. The bar had to be handcrafted. The ceilings in the place were probably fifteen feet tall, with moldings engraved in the ceilings and marble floors under my feet. I sat there pondering the day and enjoying a double jack on the rocks when a beautiful blonde came and sat next to me, we got to talking and it ended up that she was a town planner of Aspen why she was sitting next to a degenerate like me I don't know her name was Reilly Timmons she told me a little about what she did for the town and how she did a lot of the entertainment planning in the town. We kicked it off rather well, she asked me what I was doing in town and I told her that I was a writer looking for a good story and that I thought Aspen might be the place to find it. I told her how I thought the town looked like a fucking ghost town during the day and she agreed. She then slipped me her business card, telling me to come by her office sometime while I was in town. She then got up and walked away, looking back at me over her shoulder, as she walked away with a hint of desire, she really turned me on. A woman with great influence in the town and there she was singling me out of the crowd.

The following morning, I woke up and decided to go get some coffee. On the way out, I spotted some old wood snow skis on the wall. I had thought about ripping them off and going to the mountain for the day. I had to refrain myself from staying out of trouble, but that wouldn't last long. On the way there, I took the long way walking around Aspen; the streets were barren. I thought that this was strange for a town like this. All these storefronts and not even one of them opened, it really didn't matter anyway because I probably couldn't afford anything from any of the shops anyways. Again, I was looking for a bar to sit at after a rough night, but nothing, the town was barren, kind of like the whole town heard a bomb was about to go off and they all knew the times were ending as we speak I never even heard the sirens go off. I walked to the bottom of the lift in town, where I found a geometric design in the ground. I stood right in the middle of the thing and looked around. I could feel the artist's work as I stood there. I sat, taking it all in. I spun around, looking in all directions enjoying the views of the slopes. I was feeding off the design of the artist's work, taking it all in. I then took my phone out to find the nearest coffee shop and I started my walk in the direction of the place. As I got about halfway there, I felt like the flash of the bomb came over me. The light was grand, but the destruction was none to be had. But that's all, it was a flash with no destruction to be had. At that very moment, I had felt that I had braved the storm and soon after it, people started to appear on the street again. The town was expecting something to happen, or it was all a figment of my imagination. The whole thing felt real as hell to me. I felt like I had repelled the force of the bomb to help protect the place from great destruction. I got a little closer to the coffee shop and again, I was harassed by the police. There I was, just walking down the street feeling like doom was among us all and I was out braving the storm and the police surrounded me like I was the president who was about to get his head blown off by some lone assassin. It was very strange.

They swarmed me from all angles in a group of about five or six and they were looking around in all directions as if they were looking for someone in the distance, not really paying attention to me at all, just forming a human shield around me. I felt like I was about to be the next Kennedy right then and there, but the shooter had been foiled. The cops began to question me, asking me what I was doing, they were acting very strange. I told them that I was just on a walk to get some coffee. They asked me for my ID, I then took it from my billfold and handed it to them. They said that I looked like someone and I joked, saying that they also looked like someone. They said that I fit their description of someone, which I have no goddamn clue how I would fit the description of anyone. I was wearing plaid pants with a purple sweater with typewriters and clocks on it. There is no way that I looked like anyone else. I was also wearing aviators with one of those hats that the ears fold up with a kind of animal fur lining. The only person that I could possibly think of from Aspen was Hunter S Thompson. This was Aspen after all, but the man had been dead for 8 years by that time. This was Aspen, after all, and I did go to the town on a writing adventure in the spirit of the man. I thought we needed more men like him out there, the freelancers. The ones that can stir the pot a little and bring fun and excitement to the world, it was if I was being welcomed back. As the cops were talking to me, I could not hear a single word any of them said other than a cute little cop. I was trying not to flirt with her too much, but I couldn't resist. I lowered my shades a little to look at her, she was beautiful. She began telling me that there was some sort of break-in in the area and the man who did it had cut himself and was covered in blood, terrible images flashed through my mind. I then asked her how I fit the description. She looked me over with a bit of desire in her eyes and told me that I didn't match at all and that I most defiantly was not covered in blood. What god-awful cops are these to show up and treat a man in this way? I smiled at her and asked for my ID back and she handed it straight back to me. I asked her if I could proceed to get my coffee, she smiled in a very cute way and said yes. I asked her where her favorite place to get coffee was in the town and she pointed me in the direction of her favorite place. I should have asked her to join me. Once I was on my way again, I looked back at the cops and they were watching me like the secret service. I thought to myself, "SHIT MAN" I hadn't even started my day and already causing trouble "WHAT THE HELL" I hadn't even had a drink yet. I got my coffee and it was a total disappointment quality-wise. You would think in a town with so much money, you would be able to get a decent cup of Joe or a decent meal somewhere. I drank my coffee as I walked back to my hotel room. The bar was about to open, so I grabbed my typewriter and took it to the bar to get some work done. When I got there, I found a nice spot where I could set the typewriter up and relax. I ordered a Bloody Mary and began to work for a few hours having quite a few drinks in the few hours that I was there. When I had left my hotel, they told me that I did not have a room for the following night, telling me that they were booked up. They told me, though, that they would find a place for me to stay that night. The lady told me when I arrived back from the bar that she had found me a room right down the road for 89 dollars a night. "GREAT" I thought, no more stresses of finding a room. I was soon to be disappointed, though. I walked into the place, they had a nice heated pool outside and I thought this would be a good place. The girl at the desk was maybe 22, a beautiful Latina woman. I told her that my other hotel had told me that they had a room for me for 89 dollars. She walked me to the room to show it to me. When she opened the door, it looked like a goddamn jail cell with four beds in one room, I looked at the girl working and told her that this room just wouldn't do. I told her that the other hotel told me that I had a room for 89 dollars, not a jail cell; she chuckled a little and told me to follow her back to the front desk to see what she could do. She told me that I could get the suite for 200 dollars a night and I told her I didn't need the suite. I looked out the window and saw a room with the door open poolside there was a table and chairs right outside the room with the pool only about ten feet from the door. I said what about that one. She told me that it had just become available. "GREAT" I said. She walked me to the room to show it to me, there were two beds and a small kitchen. I told her that I didn't care what was in the room I just liked the table out front. She looked at me strangely and laughed. I put my things down in the room and then set up an office outside next to the pool. I had a pack of smokes, a bottle of booze and a couple of joints that I had rolled earlier. For it being winter, it was surprisingly warm next to the pool. I had no swimsuit, but I had a pair of Long Johns that I got in the pool with. The manager rushed out shortly after seeing me in the pool with the Long Johns on and informed me that they had complimentary swimsuits and asked me for my size, telling me that he would grab me a pair right away. I thanked the man and he arrived with them briefly. I made myself a drink and sat down at the table. The other guests started arriving from the slopes and were showing up at the pool. I began offering drinks and pot to almost all of them, I didn't have much money, but I still insisted on sharing with all of them, but only one person took a beer, and another took a pull of my whiskey. After the people warmed up to me a little, I sparked a joint and got back into the pool with it. We all sat around and passed the doobie. Quite a few people enjoyed a part of it, to my surprise even some of the older generation was enjoying it. We ended up having a very good time. I was talking with folks learning where they were from and what they did for a living. How a group of degenerate Americans like us wound up in the same pool, I don't know. To my surprise, there were a lot of folks from Lake Michigan, it seemed like the lost crew of the Edmond Fitzgerald, but in fact we were never really lost at all. We had just moved on, it seemed like it was a reunion of lost friends. This time though, we were not sinking, we were just sitting back enjoying ourselves once again. There was a mother and daughter there from Germany, the woman's daughter was pure bliss. She didn't say much, but I tried not to let her catch me staring at her out of the corner of my eye.

I got out of the pool and decided to walk into town to get some food to cook in the room. The weather was nice that day and the sun was quite warm. I found a local meat and cheese shop and I walked in and got some sausage and another bottle of booze. I then walked to the grocery store next door and got a piece of salmon and some greens. As I was walking up to the register, I had spotted the girl from the bus a couple of nights prior. She was a couple of spots up in line. At least, I thought that it was her I had been drunk that night. She looked back and noticed me and gave me a smile. I said hi to her and asked if she had remembered me from the previous night. We talked for a little bit and she said she was headed home. I regret to this day not asking her to join me for dinner because I had plenty of food for two in my bag. There she was, a woman of passion and love and we met on two freak occasions and I let her slip away.

I made my way back to the hotel and cooked my dinner and ate. Afterwards, I decided to go back to the pool for an evening dip; the German girl was in the pool swimming and I sat next to the pool, writing, observing her as she swam alone in the pool. I didn't manage to get much done with that kind of distraction around. After a while, one of the other guests came out to the pool and saw my joint on the table and asked me if I would spark it up. I had no problem doing so; we smoked the joint and I talked to him about going to the woody creek tavern for a drink. I told him that the author that was my inspiration used to frequent there often. He said, "HELL YES" he even told me that he would buy my drinks for me. I went back to my room and changed, we took a pull off my bottle and we were on our way to the bar. As I walked in, the focus of the bar was on me, for some reason, I sat down at the bar and ordered a Bloody Mary. My new friend was drinking beer and asked me why the hell I was drinking Bloody Mary at this time of day. I told him to fuck off in a joking manner. At that point, I reached in my pocket and pulled out a couple of stickers that I had acquired from the pot shop there in town. I proceeded to slap one down right on the top of the bar. A few minutes later, the bartender came by and asked me if I had put that there. I told him that I didn't, but I did tell him that I saw the bastard that did it and he was a very deranged-looking man and to not mess with him. As I sat there watching the man peel the sticker from the bar top, he struggled as it pulled off in little pieces. He finally got it off and walked away, but what the fucker didn't know is that I had one more in my pocket and as soon as he walked off, I slapped another one down in the same spot. My friend started laughing hysterically and we ordered another round. When the bartender came to serve us our drinks, he saw the new sticker on the bar and snapped at me like a deranged beast yelling at me, asking if I thought that it was funny. I told him that I thought it was hilarious and that I was advertising for local businesses and that I found that place on the bar to be the best placement for the advertisement. He looked confused when I said that and acted like he was going to kick me out, but I put the fear in him and he walked away, leaving the sticker this time. The rest of the night was a blur; from there on out, many more drinks were to be had and we made the trip back to the hotel. I really don't remember the trip, but I do remember getting back late at night and the pool was looking rather good. I craved a late-night swim. I looked out my window to make sure none of the guests would see me jump in the pool. The coast was clear and I rushed out stark naked and jumped into the pool. I sat there for a few hours drinking and watching the stars, it was quite nice. I kept thinking about the cute German girl coming out to join me. I eventually got out of the pool and went to bed after smoking a few cigarettes in the room, which was probably a big no, but I really didn't care about that.

When I woke up the next morning, I ran into all the guests from the night before, getting breakfast and coffee. They all greeted me with smiles after enjoying themselves the night before. I walked up to the counter of the hotel office and asked if I could extend my stay another night. The man at the desk told me that they were booked up for the night and I would have to leave. I could tell there was something fishy. I sat in the lobby drinking my coffee and I overheard the manager on the phone telling me that they had a room open to someone else over the phone. I then walked up to the desk after overhearing the conversation and I told the man that I would like to get the room that he was talking about. He then told me that I was kicked out for no good reason. All the guests from the night before were looking at the manager, wondering why the man was being a prick. I guess my extreme partying ways and excess of booze and pot were too much for him to handle, "NO FUN ALLOWED IN THIS PLACE, I

GUESS" but I was happy that the people by the pool were on my side, they seemed to thoroughly enjoy themselves. As I walked away from the counter, I asked the manager what his name was and told him that I knew the owner and I was going to have him fired. He laughed and told me his name. I can't remember what it was, but I snapped back at him, saying that he looked more like a Richard. I could hear a few of the people in the lobby snicker at my remark, if you don't know Richards go by dick sometimes and he proved to be a real dick.

Well at this point, I was really feeling fucked. No more room in this god-forsaken town. I walked all over the place from hotel to hotel, trying to find a room. All the cheap rooms were sold out and the cheapest room after that was around 250 for a night, which I was not willing to pay. I imagined the hotel manager put out a word to the other hotels not to give a degenerate like me a room anywhere, or at least it felt like that. I didn't have much to do that day other than find a new room for the night as I walked around and was getting rather tired carrying my bags around town. I went into a different hotel to ask them if they had a room and they told me the price and I said that it would be the last of my funds if I were to have to pay their price. I tried to negotiate on the price and they said they could not. They seemed like they felt for me, but they were not the owners, so they couldn't make the call. I asked them if I could sit in their lobby for a little bit and they said that they would let me stay for a bit. I sat down in their lobby and they told me that I could get some coffee, so I got up and got myself a cup. I pulled my typewriter out and began to get some work done. The people in the lobby were drawn to the typewriter, like it was some sort of foreign object. The people were drawn to the thing clacking away. This is one of my favorite things about working in public with the thing. The downfall is I don't get much work done, but the plus is I normally get to meet some very interesting people and get to learn some of their stories as well. I had met a couple and they had asked me if I had gotten the chance to go up on the slopes to ski. I told him that I had not been able to afford it and the couple looked disappointed. I said it's just too god damn expensive, they both agreed then I told them how I had examined how to remove the wood skis from the 20s off the wall in my previous hotel room and hiking up the mountain. The old man laughed and told me hell, a young buck like you could get away with something like that, but that I would only be able to get one run in if I had to hike up. We finished talking and I decided to pack up and head to the pub. On my way there though, I passed a ski shop and decided to walk in. There was another beautiful girl at the counter and she rushed over and asked me if she could help me find something. I asked if they had any snowboards, but I guess the hoity-toity bastards of Aspen really don't like them on the mountain saying that they tear the mountain up, but I'm sure it's just some blasphemous scheme to keep the young generation off the mountains. I then joked with her a bit, telling her that I needed the most expensive pair of skis in the building. She looked at me a little shocked, but she played along and pulled a pair she thought was good off the rack, she began telling me about the skis and their features, but I hadn't a clue about what she was saying. I told her ok, I'll take them, but if a man is going to pay that kind of money, first I would need A test run with them, she then told me that they didn't offer that and my response was how am I supposed to pay for the most expensive skis in the place if I can't even try them out. I could see in her eyes that she would have let me take them if it was her store, but the company she worked for would not have such a thing. I acted disgusted and walked out, but she smiled at me, knowing that I was playing the whole time, probably wondering what a man like me was doing in Aspen. It didn't look like they had much business, so she was happy that someone came into the store.

I feel as if I stick out like a sore thumb in this town, but I get a sense of enjoyment out of not fitting in. That just means I'm not one of the sheep and they are getting worried. Again, I was walking through this town of gloom all these stores and none open because the town is too expensive for the population that works it. I went from hotel to hotel, getting the same story. Negotiations on the price of rooms were off the table since none of these people worked for themselves. They all worked for someone who lived in Switzerland and came to their hotel once a year if that. I went into a local restaurant for lunch and when I went to pull money out of my pocket, I reached in and pulled my hotel key out. This was an actual key and not a shitty card you get at most hotels. I was sure of it that they didn't change the locks on the door. This gave me an idea, fuck, maybe I could sneak back into my room from the night before. Fuck the Richard working at the desk, just maybe I can get away with it. I walked back to the hotel to scope it out to see if I could possibly get away with it. I showed up and sat at the table that was outside my room from the night before and I started to write. I had peace for about thirty minutes before the ass hat of a manager came out telling me that I had to leave. I told the bastard that because of him, I could not find a room anywhere for the night. He shouted at me once more to leave the premises. I told him to fuck off and leave me alone; he threatened to call the police, I told the bastard to call them and that I had already met them all and knew them well. I didn't have a worry in the world. He rushed back inside, looking like his head was about to explode from pure anger. To tell you the truth, I had lost respect for the man when he kicked me out. So, I really didn't give a shit about the whole ordeal. I sat and continued writing for a good 20 minutes or so while I waited for the cops to show up. I smoked a cigarette and about the time I was done, a patrol car pulled up. I lit a second one right off the first, feeling like I would need it to talk with these swines. But to my surprise, the cops were very cool. I had told them about the ordeal with the hotel and that I couldn't find another room in the town to save my life. They gave me the names of a few hotels to call but all the ones they had mentioned I had called or walked to. They were asking me what I was writing. I told them that I was in search of the American dream, but Richards such as this manager, make it hard to find. The manager stood there looking like he was about to explode because they weren't roughing me up and hauling me off in handcuffs. They were just sitting there talking with me, looking like they were about to take a seat because of pure curiosity. They probably don't run into many weirdos, such as me writing on a typewriter about looking for the American dream and I felt like they wanted a good part in my story, not to be portrayed as the bastard cops they show on the media but as real human beings with hearts. As we sat and talked, we forgot the manager was even there. Then one of the officers turned around and saw the red-faced manager and spun around with a half-smirk and said that we should probably head out. The man who had brought me to a woody creek tavern was in the pool as I was being escorted out. He yelled at me as I walked by, saying he had my back and that he just wanted to make sure I wasn't mistreated. I picked up my things and my typewriter and thanked the good man for the drinks at the bar and for looking out. He said, "GODSPEED BROTHER." The cop had me get into his patrol car, he informed me that I wasn't in any trouble at all, I just had to leave the property. I shut my door and we drove off out of nowhere. I asked him if I could stay at his place for the night, he thought about it for a while and then he said that his wife probably wouldn't like him bringing a stranger home to stay the night. He pulled over about two blocks from the hotel and told me to get out of the car and, at the same time, handing me his business card. He told me if I could not manage to get a room I could go to the local home-less shelter in Snowmass. I told him that I was, in fact, not homeless and that I had money. He told me I should at least go over there and that they have very good food and it's free. He said I had to get there by a certain time to sign up to sleep in the church and if I didn't, they would not let me in. He smiled big and said that I mustn't tell them that I have any money. He told me that they wouldn't let me in if I did. He also told me that if I ran into any more trouble in town, to give him a call. I shook his hand and he wished me good luck finding the American dream and said, "I HOPE IT'S STILL OUT THERE TO FIND." As I got out of the car, he pointed me towards the bus stop to Snowmass.

I had decided to go check out the homeless shelter. I hopped on the first bus and was on my way. I pulled into the place where the officer told me to go. As I walked in, I was greeted like I was some sort of scum. I was led into the place where all the homeless ate. There were tons of good-looking food and loaves of bread of all sorts. I sat down at the table with my typewriter and all the people there had been looking at me since I was the new guy. I sat and explained my story to these people and they asked about the typewriter. I told them that I was out to find the American dream and I planned to write about it. They gathered around the thing like it was something foreign and strange. A few of them asked if they could type a few things, I didn't have a problem with it at all. I let them glamor at the thing as I had to fill out plenty of paperwork. The funny thing is like the people who ran the place talked to me, they knew there was something strange about me. They treated me rather poorly till I told them that I really appreciated what they were doing for these people, giving them a place of warmth and good food. I then did exactly what the cop told me not to do and I told them that I had money and just wasn't able to find a room in town for a good price. I threw them off when I told them that I would like to donate to their cause, but they explained to me that they were very well funded and that they had more food and funds than they knew what to do with. I told them that I was out to write about the American dream and that I felt I was kicked out of the town to see if it was there. Luckily, they didn't seem to care that I had money and they decided to let me stay the night anyway and that we all would be moved to a church where we would sleep for the night. They informed me that I had to be at the church by ten that night, otherwise they lock the doors and would not let me in; they also told me that it was a drug and alcohol-free place and that they could give me a breathalyzer and deny me access if I was to fail. I agreed to their terms just to get them off my back and returned to the room with the others. There was a man cooking us all food in the kitchen. It was part of the same room that we were sitting in and as I sat and talked with the folks there about how we all wound up in this place. We all waited to be fed. The funny thing about it was that the food they served us was ten times better than any of the food that I had eaten in town and even worse, I had to pay for the slop, and here I was sitting in a homeless shelter feasting on great food. We all sat down at a large table and ate family-style, it was damn good. After our meal, I decided to leave the place, knowing that I had to be at the church by ten, so I took the first bus back to Aspen and went to the local bar for a drink and to continue my work, knowing damn well that they might not let me back in with the stench of alcohol on my breath but I thought to myself "WHAT THE HELL" I have gone this far so why not take it clear to the edge.

After a few drinks at the bar, I had to make my way back to the church to get my place to sleep. When I showed up, the doors were locked and the place looked baron and deserted while the whole town seemed full of life. I really didn't want to go to the church, I wanted to be out with my people, running amuck on the streets. The police station was across the street, so I walked over and tried to walk in, the building had double doors in front and the first set was unlocked. I stepped inside and the next set of doors was locked. The place looked deserted except for a cleaning lady who saw me through the glass doors, but she just kept cleaning, looking over at me every now and again to see what I was doing. Since I could not figure out how to get into the church, I figured what the hell, I'll just sleep here for the night inside the front doors of the police station. I figured this would not be a problem and that it should be a safe place to stay. After a little while, I assume the cleaning lady called someone and an officer walked into the corridor from outside. He asked me what I was doing there, and I told him that I had signed up for the homeless shelter, but I could not find a way into the church. After talking to the officer for a while, he told me that I had to go around the back of the church and the back door was open "Fuck" I thought they wouldn't even let degenerates like us use the front door of the church. I really wasn't ready to go in, yet there was a whole town of bustling people running around town. I was greeted by folks I had met where I had eaten earlier. They led me inside the church, which I was leery of even going inside. It had been many years since I had even been in a church. I feared the damn roof caving in on my skull as soon as I stepped in. To my surprise, it did not; they led me to these small empty rooms. They were barren, with nothing but a few people sitting on the floors. I set my things in a corner in one of the rooms and they led me to the basement of the church. I felt it was the end, at last they were bringing me to the catacombs where I would spend the rest of eternity. It was a very old church and the basement had a dungeon appearance to it. It smelt damp and the old stones of the foundation were seeping water through the cracks. As I walked down this damp corridor, I was led to a small room at the end with thin mats, the kind they give you in jail for the metal beds. If you have ever enjoyed the luxuries of jail, you know exactly what I'm talking about. I walked back upstairs and put my mat down. I walked around the church and looked at photographs on the walls and to study some of the history of the building, as I walked around, though, I was soon told that we were not allowed to be walking around. At that point, something didn't feel right. The reminder of jail had come back to me. I told the man to leave me alone and that I wasn't messing with anything and just looking around. I asked the man if I could go into the chapel to thank God for a place to rest for the night and he barked at me, saying that it wasn't allowed. I told the man that I could not sleep in a church that I could not go and give thanks to. The man looked at me like I was a nut and that this wasn't a normal request of the homeless. I'm not religious, but I do not disrespect any person's religion. I just felt if I was to sleep in this place, I would like to give thanks.

As I walked back to my shitty room, I opened the door and peered in; it was an awful sight that I saw. There were two others in the room now, both sitting on the floor on their little mats. I had a flashback of an insane asylum from the movies. The only thing the picture lacked was the straitjackets. As soon as I had sat down, I remembered passing a desk with a nice chair sitting in front of it. I thought to myself that this would be a far better place than to be in this room. It was nine o'clock and I had talked to my father earlier that day about getting me a bus ticket back home. He called right in the nick of time. I told him my situation that I couldn't leave the place after ten; he told me that he had got me a bus ticket and I had to go to Glenwood springs as soon as possible to check-in for my ticket. I had a great sense of relief that I didn't have to stay the night in the church. He told me that I needed to be at the bus station by three in the morning, perfect I thought, plenty of time to get out on the town and have a drink before catching the bus out of town. He seemed rather irritated when I told him that, but he soon relaxed and told me not to miss my bus.

As soon as I got off the phone, there were great tensions in the air. One of the roommates began to talk about his drug use and all the terrible things that he had done as if the man was trying to scare me, him not really knowing about my past by my looks, he probably thought that I was some weak, rich kid not knowing the true person that I am full of grit and determination not willing to take any shit off the swine in here. I maintained my composure even as I felt this man wanted to rip my goddamn throat out. Funny people they are in here.

I figured I would try and go to the desk that I had seen earlier and maybe try to get a page or two done before ten. I left the room and walked to the desk and sat down. The man running the shelter soon biting at my heels like a small dog. I swiftly kicked him off and asked him what the problem was. He muttered that I mustn't sit at the desk and I asked him why, he had no good answer. I called him a swine and walked back to my room to gather my things as he nipped at my heels the whole way. He is lucky I didn't turn around and knock him square in the jaw. It was almost ten and the bastard told me that I couldn't leave. I told the bastard he had better get out of my way and let me leave. He was a controlling bastard. He saw the seriousness in my eyes and stepped aside. I told him fuck this place, what kind of place are you running here. You must be completely loco to stand here and treat these people like shit, you are the true degenerate, now get out of my way, I have a story to write and it's a story that I must be out on the town to write. I yelled there is a local pub calling my name. I picked up my things and walked out the door with great relief.

The town had opened. There were people all over the streets as I walked to the pub. I sat down at a table at the far side of the bar, kind of in the corner, where I could see the whole establishment. Kind of like the old westerns, you got to sit in the corner to make sure you see the bastards chasing you walk in the door, so you can maintain the upper hand. I had a small table to myself where I set up my type-writer and ordered a bloody Mary. There were many folks in the place and many came over to ask me what I was doing. I sat and socialized with a few of them, telling the cute bartender to keep my drinks coming when she saw one run out. I was writing with fury describing my trip and what had taken place. I saw the local newspaper's motto and it said if you don't want it published, then don't let it happen, I took comfort in that, knowing that maybe the Aspen Times would publish my story. As I wrote more, the bartender came over and sat down. She too was very curious about what I was writing. I asked her a favor telling her that I was leaving town and that I needed my story delivered to the local newspaper in the morning. She looked at me kind of funny she said she didn't want the responsibility of delivering it, but she did tell me that she thought there were some envelopes behind the bar that I could put it in and leave at their door. I had walked into the paper earlier that day to drop off some of my stories and there was an older lady working the counter who acted as if she recognized me from somewhere. In the far part of the office, there was a room with what looked like a journalist having a meeting. They saw me walk in with my typewriter in hand, looking at me drooling with the idea of a good story walking in the door. I handed the older lady at the front desk my portfolio. She told me that she would give it to the editor to look. She had a big smile on her face as I walked out. I felt it was imperative that I got the rest of my story there before I left town. I got the envelope from the bartender and folded up my work and placed it inside. It was time to leave this godforsaken town and catch my bus to Glenwood.

I was rather drunk now. I walked to the paper and left my envelope at the door of the place and walked to the bus stop. I feared that someone would steal my work right out of the door, with much hesitation, I left it there anyway. On the front of the envelope, I wrote "if you don't want it published, don't let it happen" as I waited for my bus to Glenwood, I really didn't want to leave, but my ticket out was waiting for me in Glenwood. As I sat at the bus stop, the town was full of excitement that night, unlike I had seen the last few days. The bus driver who picked me up had a strange resemblance to Sam Elliot, a man I looked up to from the film industry. He kept glaring at me through the rearview mirror as I sat fading in and out of sleep. I awoke to the sound of the intercom announcing the stop for owl farm, a place I would have liked to visit. I hoped the bus would have stopped right at the good doctor's, Hunter S. Thompson's house. I always wanted to visit a place where an author sat and created his work. I told the driver that I was very tired and the stop I needed to get off at and asked him to wake me up if I was to be sleeping. The rest of the trip was a faded memory of nodding in and out of sleep till arriving at my stop. I got off the bus at the gas station that was supposed to have my ticket.

I walked in and there was a young punk behind the counter. I told him that I needed my bus ticket printed off and he told me that they did not print tickets there. I told him that he was full of shit. I asked the kid if this was the gas station where the buses came, and he said that it was. I told the kid that this was, in fact, the place where you buy tickets and they must be able to print them off. The kid looked at me dumbfounded. I had a confirmation number on my cell phone and I was hoping that I would be able to show the bus driver this to get on board. I sat at the gas station waiting for the bus and I stepped outside to smoke a cigarette. The gas station employee stepped outside to pick up the trash, telling me that I could not go inside unless he was in there. I sat outside for quite some time, waiting for the kid to perform his duties. As I waited, I had the urge to go to the bathroom. I waited and waited as he took his sweet ass time. "FUCK IT" I thought, I'm going in. I walked in and went straight to the bathroom to relieve myself. As soon as I walked out of the gas station, a punk was sitting there foaming from the mouth, just waiting to pounce on me as soon as I came out of the bathroom just, so he could use some bullshit sense of authority that he had being a gas station employee on me. He started out being very vulgar with me, yelling and telling me that he told me not to go inside I ignored his fury and simply said "I NEEDED TO USE THE BATHROOM" this infuriated the little bastard more, but he soon shut his mouth. The bus was about to arrive, as it pulled up, I walked over to the bus explaining to the driver about the punk kid who didn't know how to work the ticket machine and that I had a confirmation number for my ticket on my phone. The driver looked at me funny as if he had never experienced such a problem. He told me that he could not accept the confirmation number. I told him he must be kidding, I asked the man to use his computer on the bus to make sure that I could ride. You would think today that the technologies would be far superior and that this should be a simple task. We sat and talked for quite some time as if the man was going to let me on the bus. I only had enough money for one or two more nights of hotels tops, so I was getting concerned. He again said I couldn't ride, and I thought, thank God, this damn bus is probably going straight over the edge of the mountain later tonight, so maybe I lucked out. I walked away and watched the bus leave for its perilous doom over the edge.

I looked at my phone to find the nearest hotel for the rest of the night. I found one only about a mile or two from the gas station I was thinking about walking. About that time, a Mexican man pulled up in a white van I decided to ask the man for a ride. To my surprise, the man agreed. I offered the man some cash for the ride, but he would not take it. I threw my bags in the van and off we went towards the hotel. As we got close, I could tell that it was a newly built hotel because there was still all the construction equipment in the parking lot. It really looked like a nice place, I thanked the man for the ride and he wished me luck.

I walked to the front door of the newly built place and to my surprise, the automatic door swung open right towards me, almost knocking my teeth out. I thought to myself, who put this goddamn door in backwards. I walked up to the counter, ready to get some rest for the night. It was probably around 4 or 5 in the morning. At this point, the lady told me that the check-in time wasn't till 11 and that she couldn't get me a room till then. I asked the woman if there was anything she could do to explain my situation at the bus stop and that I badly needed a place to lay my head for the night. She apologized and said that there was nothing that she could do. I asked if I could rest in the lobby till check-in and she told me I could not. "GODDAMN IT" how hard is it for a man to find a place to rest around here? By the looks of the place, I was quite excited to stay there. They had a large heated pool and everything; I asked the lady if I could go sit by the pool till check-in. She again said no, I thought I just about had her when I asked her if she would like to go skinny dipping in the pool with me, she smiled very big and I could tell that she was deeply considering the idea. She said she had to watch the front desk. I looked at her and said for what reason the only people who were in this place at this hour were the two of us. She thought for a minute, then said she would probably lose her job if the owner was to watch the surveillance cameras of the two of us having a late-night skinny dip in the pool. I told her to hell with the owner, he would probably try to sell the footage to make a buck, and she laughed. I asked her once more if there was anything she could do, and she said there wasn't. I told her I must leave then and try to find a nearby hotel; she felt bad, I could see it in her eyes. I'm sure if it was her hotel, she would have let me get a room with no hesitation, hell she probably even would have partaken in the late-night skinny dipping.

I knew on the drive to the hotel I passed a whole string of hotels. I thought they were only about a mile down the road, so I left and started walking. I guess the miles flew by as I was talking to the man who had given me the ride, because it was more like a three-mile walk. As I was walking down the cold dark road, I had to carry my typewriter and a rather bulky duffle bag, it was quite the chore. I remember thinking how nice it would be if a car was to drive by and offer me a ride, but that never happened. I then began thinking about a deranged cougar lurking in the shadows along the side of the road, but at that point, I really didn't care if I was to be mauled by a beast of nature, it wouldn't be a bad way to go I thought to myself. I walked past an entrance to a country club and I thought to myself how nice it would be to get to play some golf, maybe tomorrow, I thought. I had the whole day to kill anyway because the next bus wasn't coming till three in the morning again. I finally got to the first hotel in the string of them all. I walked up to the door and the place had the lights off, but there was a doorbell to ring that said for late night use. I looked around and rang the bell no lights came on, so I tried again once more with the same outcome. I decided to sit down on the front stoop of the place and plug in my phone because it was about to die. As I sat on the stoop charging my phone, a deranged-looking old lady came out the side door of the place in her robe and demanded me to tell her what I was doing. I told her that I needed a room for the night and she barked back at me that they were closed. I told her that I knew that, but the door had the doorbell on it for late-night use. I had a strange feeling that no one had used the doorbell in years as the lady seemed to have forgotten that the thing was even there. I began to ask the old woman if I could get a room and she immediately started barking at me to leave the property. I'm glad the woman didn't have a gun because she probably would have shot me right there on the spot. I pulled the charger from the wall and grabbed my things and left quickly. "FUCK IT" I thought off to the next one, I started to wonder if I was ever going to get some sleep that night, hell, the sun was about to come up. Not too far down the road, there was another hotel and to my surprise, there was a available vacancy sign lit up with neon. There was an antique fire truck in the parking lot for advertisement, it gave me a good feeling about the place. I walked into the lobby of the hotel and there was a very nice woman at the desk. I probably looked like I was dead, and I told her that I desperately needed a place to sleep, telling her that I was very exhausted from the previous day. It was now morning and the sun was popping up over the horizon. She looked at me, kind of funny, wondering why I was on my deranged trip, but she shrugged it off and said that she would give me a room. I went into my room and I managed a few hours of sleep till the sun came gleaming through the half-opened blinds. I got up out of bed and opened them all the way up. There was a great view of the mountain across the valley. There was a large red mountain with an American flag blowing in the wind at the top. I went into the lobby of the hotel and got some coffee and went back to my room to get to work.

· · ·

Hunter S. Thompson and his spirit is being washed from the town that he helped to make different and unique by the money thirsty "SWINE"

"IT'S A DANM SHAME AND DISGRACE TO THE GOOD DOCTOR"

13

THE BREAKDOWN

Here I was, trying to maintain focus washed up and running low on fuel. I gave Aspen the best that I had, I handed in papers to the Aspen press just to see what they might think, and I decided to get out of town before the bastards made me sleep in a church. I had to get out of there. The town was sucking the life right out of me and no one wanted any fun. I made it to Glenwood springs barely even going. I wondered how long it would take Aspen times to go through my work. I wondered what the bastards were doing, did they get any of my work? Or were they just standing in circles around all the pages I had written, shredding them into little pieces and dancing like ghosts around a campfire, burning them, trying to stay warm? I wrote things in there like freedom of press just to see if they would make a stand and publish some of my work to stir the pot. I had read some articles in their paper and it was all rubbish. They could really use some excitement in there. But for me, I got straight to the truth of the town; they are a bunch of monsters who want to kick the young generation out with their money. Or to try and make monsters out of us all, but I see some good people in the town and they are the ones barely scraping by. They might as well throw community out of the equation as well because there is not much community to be had. The whole town is bought up and no one can truly afford to live like this. Might as well throw the paper out the window, for they have no one to read it. It's just full of rubbish anyways.

Dear Jesus, have we all gone mad? The media and mess on TV are distorting our minds. We need more John Wayne's out there, not the fucking clown kind. God only knows why they put this rubbish on TV, but the era of quality life and good morals is long gone with no hope of bringing it back and I wish I knew why. I can't even watch TV anymore. Bad jokes and rubbish people just rewrite the same old stories with no new twists.

For the last few days, I was in search of the truth and I managed to find it. No one feels safe anymore, they have all been shown on TV and through the media that the world isn't safe anymore. No more hitch-hiking free love and spirits, they are still out there but few and far between. I had worked hard for my trip and was kicked out for having little money but high spirits. I wish I had high spirits this morning. No booze around either what kind of way to go is this. I was not done yet in Aspen, but the money ran out. There are problems all around us, but people turn a blind eye to them but to me, they are so obvious. One thing I would like to see would be better products for consumers and get rid of all the throwaway items, especially the throwaway razors. I had to shave in Aspen and it took me three of the things just to clean up, if we would make good products, that would be the best thing for recycling. Make things as good as my damn type-writer it's a 1946 and still rolling away. I wish we still maintained the made in America motto of making some of the best products. It's a shame how money screws everything up. I wish I was a blender salesman and sold one good blender instead of making three different shitty ones that need to be replaced every few years. With the use of a little extra material, we could have good things again and not have to waste the energy of making three, saving us money and getting us that much closer to the American dream again, be able to save money and have keepsakes to pass down to the future genera-tions. This idea is a good one, but people must step up to achieve it. I really don't know what people think of me nor do I care, but I find it funny I have been peaceful long enough and I wish I could shove it in their faces that we are buying literal shit. I don't think I'm a mad man but a man of vision, so god damn, it keeps giving up your rights because soon there will be none left. I refuse to give up mine, though. I want to see real fun again, the renegades, it's our time to fire back and I have been working on this for a very long

time.

I started to wonder what kind of trip this was turning into, was I supposed to be here? Why had I come out here? Then I realized, oh yeah fellow comrades, and I came out here to find it. Some people asked me what "IT" was and I told them the American dream. The true reason everyone comes to this country is an opportunity to make things better for ourselves. I shouted "listen, damn it" this could be the last chance we have, but no one seemed to care anymore. I was sitting back in my room, trying to decipher what I saw the last few days and the experiences that I had. I was feeling rather tired. I hadn't really slept in a couple of days, so I was on edge. I looked around my hotel room to look for a possible place to hang myself to end all the madness, but there was no way that the cheap towel racks and coat hooks would support my weight. The cheap products even prevent you from killing yourself. Now, I really wasn't going to hang myself, but I felt like hell and it didn't sound so bad at the time. I would get some good sleep for a little while like that, I think. I was having writer's block and contemplating hanging myself in my hotel room, so I decided to get up and go for a walk to the bus station to get my ticket, so I wouldn't go through the same shit I did the night before. It was a beautiful morning with clear skies and bright sun, instantly lifting my spirits as I walked out the door. I got a couple of blocks down when I spotted a taco truck. I was feeling rather hungry, so I decided to stop and eat. I looked at the front of the taco truck and it said cash only and it was a very clean trailer. These guys, I thought, are on the right track for the American dream, just trying to get by selling tacos, so I decided to see what it was all about. I was in Aspen the last few days and hadn't managed to get a good meal anywhere, and here are these two guys selling tacos out of a trailer "kudos to you, my friends" I ordered two beef tacos and sat down to eat. As I took my first bite, I said "DAMN, THIS IS SOME GOOD SHIT" much better than anything I had managed to eat in Aspen and these guys were working out of a trailer. I thanked the men and told them that they had very good food. I began back towards the bus station and right behind these guys' trailer was a restaurant that had been closed. It was barren, with no one occupying it at all. It made me sad to see these Mexicans and there stand with an empty restaurant right next to them. The food was great, and I wished that these men could have the thing to run their business from. Like I said, it was the best food that I had found in these mountains all weekend. I hate seeing these mountain towns being bought out because the people like these guys with good ideas couldn't afford the building because it probably costs a small fortune. So, it will be UN occupied till someone tears it down and builds a chain restaurant there another cookie-cutter establishment.

Heading back towards the bus stop, I looked at this car dealership and instantly recognized the name on the building, Phil Long. I had remembered meeting him a few years back on one of my ski trips. I think it was sunlight. I really can't remember what got us talking, but he offered me a job and gave me his phone number. I thought to myself, this is weird, I should see how the old boys are doing, but first I had to make sure that my bus ticket was secured. I made it to the gas station with the bus stop and told the manager of the inconvenience that I had the night before and she apologized and printed my ticket. I wish the punk would have been there, so I could give him a piece of my mind. I headed back to my hotel to finally get some rest but first, I wanted to stop in and see Phil. I walked in and was greeted by a Mexican maiden she was beautiful, and she resembled my high school crush, so I felt right at home with her. I told her that I was interested in possibly trading my 53 Buick or one of my boats for a cheap car. She smiled and said she could see what she could do. She called another man over to ask him if they could do anything and he told her they could not. Then I interrupted telling them that I knew

Phil Long and that we were good friends, now this was a bit of exaggeration because I had only met the man for about an hour and had a few drinks with him but as soon as I said that the man turned to me and said one moment. He proceeded to go get a different man for me to talk to and the man who showed up next was wearing a suit and asked to see what I had to offer. I showed him pictures of my boats and cars and he told me that he had an appraiser in Kansas City who could come and take a look; he said he would give me a call in the next few days. Hell, that was easy. I thanked the man and the Mexican maiden, then asked what kind of vehicle I was interested in. I told her the most expensive one they had. She asked me if I wanted to take any cars for a test drive and I held back the urge to tell her I would like to take her on a test drive. She was a fine specimen, one of God's great creations, I told her that I really was just there to see if Phil remembered me. She smiled and gave me a hug before I walked out the door. I have never had that kind of service from a saleswoman, but it was much appreciated.

I left the dealership and went back to the hotel, asking them for some leniency since I had checked in at 6 or 7 in the morning if I could stay till three that night for the price of one night. To my surprise, the woman said that was fine. I slept another couple of hours and heard the neighbors causing a ruckus in the room next to mine. Somehow I had forgotten to pick up some beer while I was out. I decided to knock on the door to see if they had any beer. They opened up the door and laughed as the room billowed smoke and told me they did not. Luckily though, I had some pot, so I smoked a little to take the edge off. This put me right back to sleep. I almost slept too late I woke up and had to pack my things in a frenzy to get to the bus stop in time. I took out of the room like a shot from a gun and thanked the lady at the front desk as I ran out the door. I was hurrying to the bus stop and decided to stop at a gas station to get some beers for the bus ride. I grabbed a case from the cooler and brought it to the counter. The lady at the desk told me that they could not sell alcohol at that time because it was too late at night. I was thoroughly disappointed, and the woman could tell as I brought the case back to the cooler. I thought about just running out with it and throwing money down on the floor. I looked at the woman working, and I felt like she knew my intentions of stealing the beer, but she gave me a look to go for it. I didn't know if I could put these people through that kind of strain and I didn't want them to lose their jobs for letting me steal a case of beer. I guess it would not have been stealing if I had thrown money on my way out, but I didn't want to risk it for their sake. I left feeling rather bummed about not getting any beer and got back to the bus station to wait. I had shown up about an hour early and met a young girl and her daughter at the stop, they too had to wait for their bus, but they were heading to California. We sat and waited there and talked. I was playing with the girl and her daughter. We were causing a ruckus with the stuffed animals in the place, making the employee rather annoyed, but we didn't care. The girl was getting a kick out of how well her daughter liked me. She told me that her daughter was normally shy and wondered why she liked me so much. I really didn't know, but her daughter was giving me hugs and I started throwing her up in the air and catching her. She was loving it and so was her mom. It was quite nice talking to them A bit of relief to have someone to talk to. Their bus showed up and we had to say our goodbyes, but before I did, I bought the little girl the stuffed animal that she kept playing with.

After they left, I had another 15 minutes before my bus was to arrive.As it pulled in, I rushed out to get on board right away to ensure my ticket was valid and working. When I got to the bus, the old boy driving hardly even looked at my ticket. When I got on the bus, it was an awful sight. I felt I might be sick from being so cooped up like farm-raised chickens. There were a lot of people sleeping, so to not disturb any of them with seats next to them, I walked clear to the back of the bus. I found a place in the very back. It wasn't a seat at all, but there was a little shelf I sat on. At least I had a place to work. I thought I had been on some sort of a writing frenzy the last 24 hours. I sat in the back of the bus like some sort of degenerate. I couldn't help thinking to yell upfront at the driver to floor this goddamn bus and let's see how far we can jump the thing right off the side of the mountain. The world would never care if a bunch of degenerates went flying off the cliff. Half the people on the bus were sleeping anyway. I could sense the bus driver was deeply considering flooring this damn bus, I could picture the speedo climbing; I thought about asking him if he thought the thing could even go 100 miles an hour. I don't think he has the nerves for excitement like that, you know, it could be like the DeLorean, we might just leave the planet. The ratio was all wrong, though if I was going to go out with a group of people, I would like for the man/woman ratio to be a little better, if anything more women, please. Just in case reincarnation is real, I want to come back with a bunch of women. I hope the appraisers meet me in Kansas City. I just can't wait to get home to see where this long strange trip has taken me.

I put in a call to the Aspen news editor and left a message asking the editor if he liked any of my work, but the bastard didn't pick up, so I had to leave a message asking if they had received the envelope that I left in the door, I hope so. I put a lot of time into that work, the bastard better call me back soon because if they read any of it, they damn well know I built a good friendship with the local police of Aspen. I would hate to have to call them to go and pick up my works. Hell, maybe after this, I'll try to send it into the rolling stone next. The world is dying for a good story these days. I feel like I'm on a mission from God to write something worth a fuck. As we made our way through the mountains, the snow began to fall heavily; we were forced to pull over so that the driver could put chains on the bus. Once we had stopped, he saw me sitting in the back on the shelf and this angered the man, demanding that I find a proper seat, I tried to explain to the man that I sat there to not wake anybody. I have had to write on the bus by hand to keep the sound down of the typewriter. But I left the waking people up part to the bus driver. He began to yell at me for finding a spot I could sit without bothering anybody. He was very disrespectful in the way that he talked to us customers, who were now very annoyed by being abruptly awoken by this yelling man. He could have just been out putting the chains on the thing instead of disrupting us all. I hope this man in his deranged state doesn't drive the thing like the nitro express down the mountain, but if he decides to, I hope he puts this fucking thing on a straight path to an establishment that takes away our freedoms. The bus system sucks, there is no guarantee on time arrives, they are never on time for anything. What about people on a schedule? Now I really can't tell you what my schedule entails but I, in fact, have a schedule. I feel like I have very few days left, we never know when we are going away, so we all have a schedule to keep. Just this stop to put the chains on is costing me precious time.

We were finally back on the road. I had offered to help the driver put the chains on the bus, but he took it offensively. As we got going, I got up to go to the bathroom and as I sat on the shitter. I could tell that he put them on loosely, I could hear one of them slapping the underside of the wheel wells. I opened the door and yelled better tell the driver that he was about to lose a chain and right as I said that, the sound went away, he had flung the chain right off. We were now stopped again I wondered if this man even knew how to drive this bus. He is only carrying around 40 lives on this thing, I hope he gets us there safe. This is probably the last greyhound that I ever take, I hope. It has been a terrible experience from the start. They only managed to cost me an extra day in the mountains and a hotel room.

I ended up being right about the chain falling off and not being properly installed. We were fortunate enough that a truck driver stopped and helped the driver install the second set of chains. I think it was the driver of Phantom 309 just stopping by to make sure that the bus made it into Denver with no issues. The folks on the bus were getting very irritated at this point and I had an idea to make these busses with a divider so that the degenerate smokers had a place where they could relax. There was a sign on the bus that said 'tell us about your driver', I feel if people read this then this driver would not get a very good review. I felt bad for the driver because greyhound obviously didn't give the man proper training.

The snow was getting thicker and I started talking about the Donner party just to liven up the terror and stimulate the thought process of this hellacious ride. I don't know if the passengers really appreciated this, but I had my fun anyway. I feel that it's a good skill to have to be able to stimulate people's minds even for the worse sometimes, just any sort of stimulation is good for these folks who have been turned off by society.

When I got into Denver, I was trying to get reimbursed for the shitty service and to be reimbursed for the hotel room I had to get the night before. They also advertised free Wi-Fi and charging for your phone and they had a lack of it all. They need to pay some people back or at least start to upgrade the busses with USB ports and some wider seats because they are so miserable to sit in shoulder to shoulder packed like sardines. I called the greyhound help line and they processed me through about 20 different people and none of them were smart enough to hear me out. It's a god-awful thing these help lines. I sat in the damn Denver bus station for almost 2 hours and was never able to get ahold of anyone on the phone who knew what they were talking about. They would just transfer me to the next person who again would transfer me. I eventually just gave up the whole thing. It was now time to board the next bus, so I was on the move again. This was a boring part of the trip because we were going across eastern Colorado and Kansas, which is all flat land and not a lot to look at. We had a stop in Limon, Colorado, for about thirty minutes, so I hopped off and went into an Abyss to get some lunch. I ordered my food and sat down to eat. They had one of those bells that you ring if you thought you had a good servicer. I kept staring at the thing, getting antsy to ring the thing as I walked out. I got up to leave and I rang the bell; the whole damn place looked up like no one had rung the bell in years, but there was nothing but smiles in the place because some strange man wanted to break the mold and ring the thing. An old farmer was sitting next to the bell and I felt I rang it to say wake the fuck up, America. I feel as if the farmer got my message. I had almost been left in Limon because I ate a little too long, the thing was about to pull out of the parking lot and I almost had to run after the thing, but I hopped on board. As we were making our way across the plains, I admired the large power-generating windmills in the distance. The conditions were perfect for these things to be running, it was a clear day and plenty of wind, but not even one of the things was turning. I sat back in my seat and was pondering why we have these things built if we are not going to run them 24/7 seems like a waste to me. So much waste anymore it makes me sick.

We were pulling into Salina and I had a sense of accomplishment. I had pulled it off, managing to break just about every rule in the book and not getting locked up. We had another stop about an hour back and I managed to get yelled at by the gas station clerk for opening my beer before I paid for it. Well, my travels just proved my point that the American dream is fucked. We really are anything but free here in the United States, the land of the, well, anything but free anymore. I wish I didn't have to leave the mountains. My work wasn't done there, but I had broken almost every rule and been kicked out of a few hotels, on top of it all, the money was running out, but I truly enjoyed every minute of the trip I got to stir the pot like a tornado rolling through a town and enlightening everyone that I met maybe not all for the better, but I showed them that if you really stand up we can be free, but when we stoop down to the system there is no real hope. I met quite a few good people out there though, people who understood my message. I was just out to let my freak flag fly and to cause a ruckus to see how far I could push it. I got close to the edge, but I managed to not go over but close enough to get a taste of what it's like to be free.

"THERE WILL ALWAYS BE TRACKS THAT SEPARATE THE MEN FROM THE BOYS. THIS IS THE TRACK THAT SEPARATES THE BRAVE FROM THE WEAK"
Jimmy Thompson

14

THE VAN FIRE

I finally got off the damn bus and it was just in time. I was going mad sitting on that damn thing. No one should have to travel like that, it truly is a terrible experience. I'm in Salina, Kansas, now waiting for my brother to pick me up from the bus stop. I sat outside smoking a cigarette waiting for him. A man from the bus stopped to talk to me. I really couldn't hear a word the man was saying to me as my mind was scrambled from the long bus ride. I proceeded to nod my head and act like I knew what the man was saying to me. About the time I finished my cigarette, my brother pulled into the lot and saved me from this man's ramblings. I told the man safe travels and quickly hopped into my brother's truck, throwing my typewriter in the back seat. Thank God I made it out of there alive I never thought that I would make it back. We headed back to my mother's house, where I had left my van that I had drove from Kansas City. I had to drive it back soon. I decided to take a rest from traveling and spent the day with my mother and brother. The whole day I was trying to get my mother to teach me how to scam my work, so I could send more to the Aspen Times. I was optimistic about the whole thing because I hate using computers, I just hate staring at a damn screen all day, it hurts my eyes. There is no heart and soul like using a typewriter and listening to the hammers pounding away with the sweet sound of the bell at the end of every line. I just enjoy it a lot more, or hell, even handwriting. I need to find a good editor. I thought about asking my mother, but she wouldn't understand the nature of my writing, it is just too farfetched for her mind to grasp. I did eventually get her to show me how to scan my work. I had a problem with the damn machine; you would think with this high-fangled tech we have, you could just put the paper in and it would work, but of course, that would be too easy. I proceeded to put the paper in every which way but the right. Everyone tells me that I need to switch to the new way of things, but until I see some major improvements, I don't see the point and refuse to spend money on that trash. I would rather just pay someone to edit my work than pay for a machine to do it. I did manage to get a few things scanned and emailed to myself. It took me a few drinks to finally calm my nerves with the ordeal of it all, it's a very stressful process, in my opinion. I decided that I needed to leave that night to get back to Kansas City to talk with my older brother about an idea that I had come up with. So, I packed my bags and off I went again. At least I had my own vehicle this time, so I was riding in comfort at least. On my way to Salina, I thought the thing was losing third gear, so I knew I at least had that going for me. Funds were very low, so I asked my mother to fill the tank, telling her that if I lost third gear, it would take me twice the fuel to get home. She looked at me funny, but I am used to driving these old vehicles that most people would call trash and I give them a second chance of getting every mile they must chug out of them. They have never really let me down; now, sure, they break down on me every now and again, but they always seem to do so in the best places possible to make the best story, so by doing so, they get to live on forever in my writing. The old 79 dodge van had done me very well for many years, it's got me through hell and back a few times and across the country twice through the mountains, but the thing is getting a little worn out. When I went outside, though, the thing fired right up and purred like a kitten. I let it warm up for a little and checked all the fluids. I should have checked the oil, but the dipstick was broken, and I had no way to do so. I added a couple of quarts before I left and figured that it would be plenty to get me back home. I was finally on the road and worried about the transmission holding out. The ride was going well. It managed to stay in third and sailed well with a tail wind. She ripped across Kansas like a comet through the sky. I was enjoying the trip with good tunes on the radio and good vibes all around. I started getting a funny feeling about the trip when I saw a truck broken down on the side of the road. The folks were flashing a flashlight at oncoming cars, trying to get someone to stop. I pulled the van off the highway, almost screeching the tires I came to a quick stop and threw the thing into reverse to get back to the truck. I met a woman and her kids. She told me that she thought that the truck had run out of gas and that her husband was walking down the highway to get help. I told the woman that I had two or three gallons in my van and that I would give her the gas to see if that would help. It was a bitter night with high winds and temperatures of about 20 degrees. I got the jug and put the fuel in her truck. I was slightly liquored up, but she didn't seem to mind. I put the gas in the truck and she hopped in and tried to crank the thing up and it refused to start. About that time, the police showed up and he ran to the back of the truck as I was getting my empty gas can. He came up to talk to me and I said something like thank God you showed up, but as I said that, he looked at me as if he had smelt the liquor on my breath, so I kindly said that I was on my way before the officer could ask me too many questions. I also neglected to tell the officer that I had a Kansas warrant out for me and had no driver's license. I really did not want to talk to the bastard, so I left in a hurry, at least he had other things to occupy him. Hell, I might have been a little drunk, but I was the only one to stop and try and help the poor people. I could only hope that the bastard wouldn't mess with me. As I left, I hoped that the officer had gotten the woman and her kids to someplace warm.

I was on the move again, getting close to warp speed, when the van started acting up. I really didn't care, I just kept it to the floor. I got within 20 miles of my house and the damn thing started smoking like a chimney out the back and slowing in speed, but my only instinct after a weeklong trip was to get home. So, I floored the damn thing and cranked up the radio to drown out the awful sounds the thing was making. As I got closer to the house, the thing was smoking worse and the engine was losing more power. I decided to pull off at an exit, but the damn thing died out at the light. I luckily got it to start back up and I said the hell with it and went straight through the light and back on the highway, giving her everything that I had. It must have really looked like a comet at that point, with a smoke trail following me as I came into the city. A tow truck came cruising by and I tried to flash my lights at them to get them to stop, but I guess he couldn't tell that I was in distress with the van billowing smoke like a steam train. He must be used to seeing that kind of thing going down the highway, even though I have only seen that kind of thing a few times in the mountains when a semi is smoking going down a grade. I got about a mile away from my house around 435 and Quivira when the thing finally put out and would go no more, so I pulled off where she quit. I pulled my phone out to call AAA and as I was doing so, smoke started billowing out from under the dash. If you have ever been in a van, you know that you are practically sitting on the engine, well the smoke was getting worse and I had to remove the engine cover. Luckily, I had a screw driver under my seat where I could remove the cover quickly. When I picked up the cover the whole engine was ablaze and all I could think about was my damn story on the dash about to go up in flames. The heat from the fire heated the inside of the van very rapidly. I didn't panic though, nothing really works me up too much anymore. I had predicted the thing burning down for quite some time since I rebuilt the engine. I was cleaning parts with gasoline and lit a cigarette with gas on my lighter and tossed it onto the table where I managed to light my van book on fire as well as the whole damn table covered in gas. It burnt the cover off the book as well as the first few pages before I could get the fire put out. After that ordeal, I had a superstition that the van was going to burn down.

At this point, flames were flaring up over the dash. If you have ever dealt with oil and gas fires, you know that you must smother them to put them out. Luckily, I had bought a few blankets at a garage sale a month before and I grabbed them up and started smothering the fire. It was hard to do, but I was determined not to let the thing burn down. Everything was catching up in flames, the spark plug wires and the engine hatch seal both caught up. The seal was dripping flaming drops onto the blankets that I was putting the fire out with, it was quite the ordeal. The blankets were burned severely and full of embers, but the engine fire was out at least. I threw the blankets out the door onto the shoulder of the highway. Thank God I thought the fire was finally out, so I sat down to cool off to try and call AAA once more, but I had lost my card in the whole ordeal. I figured I had dropped it onto the floor. I started looking for it everywhere. "DAMN IT" I lost my ticket off the side of the highway. I still could not find it anywhere. I thought that maybe I had left it on my lap and dumped it out the door when I hopped out. I jumped out of the van to look on the side of the road and when I did, the embers in the blankets outside had caught them back up in flames, being fed by the air of the passing cars. Who knows how long the things were burning out there while I was looking for my card. So now I had to put out another fire. I kept getting it out, but as the cars passed, it kept bursting into flames. Once I finally got it out, I found my card on the ground right outside my door. I moved the blankets to the back of the van, so they wouldn't take up again and catch the van back up. I had dealt with enough fire for one night. I finally got a call out to AAA and they told me that someone would be out in 20-30 minutes, so I sat and waited. Luckily the bonfire in the van had heated it very nicely, so it was nice and warm with a hint of smoke, but that didn't bother me. All I was missing were some marshmallows and I would have been set. As I was sitting there, all I was thinking about was a good girl to share some wild adventures with and only one came to mind and that was Sarah Grafton. It's funny how things can go completely wrong and the thought of that girl can bring me out of it all. The tow driver finally showed up and the fucking blankets were up in ablaze again the tow driver wasted a whole fire extinguisher to put them out, but he didn't seem to care, he didn't have to pay for it.

He told me to back away from my van as he hooked it up to the truck, but I wanted to collect my belonging out of it. I could tell he was getting a little annoyed with me because I kept hopping into the van grabbing things but fuck that guy, the damn thing almost burnt to the ground and the last thing I was going to deal with was some truck driver bitching at me. I think he understood that and let me be. I proceeded to smoke my pipe while I was waiting for him to finish up. As I hopped into his truck, I saw his pack of cigarettes sitting there. I asked him if we could smoke in the truck and the man said company policy says they are not allowed to smoke in the company vehicles. "That's a real bummer" I told him, so where do you smoke? He told me that he must pull over to smoke. What's this world coming? The truck seemed to pull the van just fine and we finally made it back to my house, I thanked the old boy for the lift and bummed a smoke off him before he left. "Not a bad chap" I thought. I shook his hand and off he went, probably wondering what a madman like myself was doing out in the world. If he only knew I was out writing for people like him, the ones who take care of others. That's what life is all about.

LONELY ROAD LONELY ROAD
I LOVE YOU SO
THE BEAUTY YOU HOLD
SEEMS TO BE UNTOLD
Patrick McAulay

15

THE TRIP TO JAIL

JULY 11

I was out late that night enjoying myself out on the town. This was usually normal for me to be out this late because I work late a lot, never getting out of bed till about three in the afternoon, a true night owl. It really doesn't matter what I have been doing all day, I'm just always up late. I decided to get out for a drink at a local bar near my house. I was planning on riding my motorcycle, which I would soon regret. I have two vehicles that I normally drive: one is the motorbike a 1980 Honda gold wing 1100, the other a 1983 Buick park avenue. The motorbike is a far superior machine for maneuverability and pure speed, two things that come in handy while trying to get out of the grasp of your local cop at three am in the morning, a far better machine for the job. For some reason, though, I decided to drive the car out that night. It too is a fine machine, it floats down the road with ease, especially with the air ride suspension and the large v8 under the hood, it's like you're driving on air, but it's still a bit of a dog when it comes to acceleration. I really don't know how fast the thing goes. All I know is that it accelerates far past the 85 posted on the speedometer. The comfort and smoothness maintain the same any way I drive it.

I had got to the bar after a long day of working on my 1952 Owens wood yacht. It's a beautiful wooden boat that I have been restoring for the last 3 or 4 months. Then helping my brother move a large playset to his house for my nieces, so I was feeling rather worn out after the day and needed a strong drink, well deserved after working like that all day. I sat down at the bar that I frequent just before it close, just enough time for one drink. As I was sitting at the bar a cute girl signaled me to come over, she was very cute and quite petite. She was with someone, so I didn't talk long other than to introduce myself. She was sitting with another guy, so I moseyed off when in all reality, I should have told the guy to fuck off since she was calling me over from clear across the room. I try to be the best man that I can be these days, but it's hard to keep my sanity like that. I used to have quite the temper, but anymore I try to stay lax. I feel like booze helps me in this way, "SOMETIMES" others it can send me into a frenzy of high-speed adrenaline driving at the end of the night. I think that every man should experience this a time or two in their lifetime. THE LAST TRUE ADRENALINE A MAN HAS. Since we have been robbed of all our other freedoms, thank God you can still get your car out on the road and push it to the max. It's a chance to let the true beast out in us all come to life, pushing things damn near to the boundaries between life and death. It's a feeling that we have all been robbed of unless you have balls and try to push for the thrill of speed. After my conversation with the girl, I slammed down my Bloody Mary and left. It wasn't even one of those top speed kinds of nights, I felt like it was a leisure drive home, but that's where the Buick gets you into trouble. The superb ride of the huge tank of the car floats down the road effortlessly with speed and style.

I had made it about halfway home when I saw the damn red and blues in my rearview mirror. "DAMN, I THOUGHT" what a bad time for the goddamn cops, also a bad time to be driving the goddamn Buick, especially because I had a warrant for my arrest from about 5 years prior. "AT THAT POINT, I KNEW THAT I WAS FUCKED" I thought to myself fuck, this car will never have the speed or the power to outrun these cops. I had a quick flash of going for it and I'm sure that I would have gotten away by showing the cops some Mario

Andretti driving skills that I have acquired over the years of high-speed driving. If push came to shove, I could have taken it on foot and that would have been the last they had seen of me, but hell, I let them have me for them to try their worst.

I pulled off to the side of the road and a Barney Fife cop appeared at my car door. He must have been a new cop because I immediately sensed his fear. I could sense it in the young cop. I'm lucky that I didn't get shot!!! He came to the window with his hand on his gun, ready to blow a man away for doing a measly 10 over the speed limit. "GOOD GOD" I thought this police force was looking rather young. I guess the good old cops got out while they could, so they wouldn't have to see the police force this way. It makes sense though, to see all the hard work and dedication you spent over the years go down the tubes to a new generation of gun-wielding juveniles no older than twenty-five raised on the show cops only seeing the worst cases. High strung, high wired, with no clue on what in the hell is really happening, ready to blast the first woman or child picking up their lipstick or their toy off the floor of the car because they have the fear and it has taken over, constant paranoia in these young cops. But I guess that's how the world is going these days, everyone is living in fear except myself. Of course, there's not much that they can do to me that they haven't done before.

So back to Mr. Fife about to be guns a blazing at any moment. Badge number 1127 of a young trigger-happy officer is at my window is asking for my id and proof of insurance. The insurance and registration were easy to come by, but I regretted giving the cop my ID. I think he needed his brownie points that night or something because the bastard was out for blood. Another cop showed up to assist him. He was an older cop who would have just let me go with a warning. I'm sure he was an older officer who probably would have given me the peace sign and said "GOD SPEED" as I drove off. But young Mr. Fife needed the arrest. I had an expired fake ID that I had managed to get in Colorado when I lived out there for a short period. I gave it to him and he took it back to his car so that he could run the thing he came back looking very puzzled. He started asking me for my social security number and I told him that I didn't know what it was. He looked at me like don't play with me I could tell that he was getting aggravated with me. He asked me over and over for my number and I kept refusing to tell him. It was a real ID, but when I was in Colorado, they spelled my last name wrong and I knew this, but when they asked me if everything was correct, I told them that it was knowing about my warrant and that the false last name might help me out at a further date. The mistake I made was that when he asked the last four digits of my social, I gave them to him and that was my biggest mistake because he didn't have shit on me till he ran the number. He went back to his car to run my name again with the last digits of my social for reference and that was it, he nailed me. He pulled up the warrants and came back to the car, telling me that I was under arrest. Well, "SHIT HAPPENS" I always told myself that in the instance that I got caught, I would just have to deal with it. I had hoped that it would have gone away since it was such an old case and that I had evaded the cops for so long they must have thought that I was doing something right. Guess I just must wait and see what the judge says. Maybe he will understand. Fife asked me to get out of the car, so I did. I hopped in the back of his car and thought, here we go again. As we sat there, the older officer came to my window and asked about my flask in-between the seats. I told the man that it was always in there. He just laughed and gave me a smile. So, there I was, they had me right where they wanted me, with a good reason to take me to jail. I think the older cop decided to give me a break about the flask and I was never given a breathalyzer or a DUI.

The car ride back to the station was a real bummer. Mr. Fife seemed to be in a rush to get back to the station. As we pulled away from the scene, he punched the car. I asked the man if that was as fast as the car went and he told me that it was damn near to the floor. "SON OF A BITCH" if that's all this car has, I defiantly could have gotten away. I should have just made a run for it, ditched the car and reported it stolen the next morning. I should have given them a run for their money. It would have been more fun for both of us. Well, maybe not for Fife. I knew there really wasn't much challenge, the young cop just didn't have the guts or the drive to be able to catch me. As we pulled into the police station garage, I had a shitty sense of Deja Vu come on about this fucking place. I went in there with good spirits though, knowing that everything would be ok. Fife was checking me in and I stared at his boots and only the toes on the things were polished. I asked him why and he said that it was easier to just polish the toe. I thought to myself, what is the point of shining your boots if you're just going to half-ass the job. I feel like if that guy was in the military that he would be on the ground doing pushups. I looked up at him and looked him in the face and told him that he could shine my boots, pointing down to a pair of worn-out work boots that I have the things hardly have any soul left on them and the steel is shining through the toes and the laces had been tied together from them breaking so many times. They couldn't be shied even if he tried without a metal polisher. Fife asked me to take them off, so I took my sweet time in doing so. Then the Fife came out of him again when he tried ordering me to place them in a brown sack. I looked at him as if he were a Joke to think that he could try and treat me this way. As if I was about to let this little 20-25-year-old cop treat me this way because he had a badge on. To me, the authority of his badge was in his boots, he might as well had socks and sandals on. You can tell a lot about a man by the condition of his boots and his hands. I looked down at my boots and at his once more and looked the cop in the face giving him no respect at all. He then immediately bent down and picked up my boots and placed them in the sack for me. I was getting arrested and the cop gave me some respect just by the sight of my boots and for being strong and maintaining my grit, at that point I finally gave old Fife some respect because he finally showed some respect to me. Respect is something that you only get as much as you give.

He took my boots and my shirt, and I was sent onto the next room. Where I was inspected, neglected and detected by the whole jail staff, it was about a 24-hour process of sitting, standing, and rearranging till they felt satisfied that I had suffered enough,—sitting on all the metal benches till my ass was chaffed from the hard seats. At one point, they moved 22 of us into maybe a 10 by 20ft room for about thirty minutes packed in like sardines. We all sat staring at each other, wondering if it was even legal for us all to be crammed in such tight quarters. Almost like we were pigs in a slaughterhouse waiting to be meat and freed from the suffering we were going through. The room was freezing cold and many people, including myself, tucked our knees into our chests to try and stay warm. There was an Indian man who was shivering profusely, and he begged every different guard for a blanket. Each one refused the man's request as he sat there shivering and begging, they just kept ignoring him. Then I felt bad for the man because other inmates, as well as the guards, were treating him like shit because he could not break the language barrier and for that, he was mistreated.

I tend to have a problem like that, I seem to think about others more than myself and I try to stand up for their rights as well as my own. At last, they finally let me out of the room full of foul odors, drunks, and degenerates, me being one of them. If there's one thing about the jail system is that nothing is fast. It takes about ten times longer than it should to get anything done around here. It took them about 24 hours before they even got me into a cell and after that wait, I was actually very happy to see a metal bed. They get you right where they want you feeling exhausted and completely worn out and abused. The sight of a bed was fantastic, it made my day no wonder they make you feel so miserable because, after that, you really start to learn to enjoy the little things in life.

After sleeping rather well on the metal bed with only an inch pad and a small blanket with no pillow. I woke after having a rather good dream about my high school sweetheart Sarah, strait to the fucking walls of hell surrounding me about 5ft away from me on either side. "FUCK" I thought to go from two completely different realities just by opening my eyes, heaven with the girl of my dreams. To an instant hell, the worst part was the urge to write and no access to paper. I guess a man as wild as the ones here have proven they cannot be trusted with such implements of power and destruction. Instead, I had to find a way to keep myself occupied. Luckily there was a book in my room, something about a couple working together to beat a computer hacker who is terrorizing some Chinese artifacts in a museum. It wasn't a bad book, I finished it rather quickly with no distractions around and I just slept like crazy for two days, sleeping in till about three in the afternoon every day. I had slept about all I could sleep and again found myself in great boredom. I had to find something to do to pass the time. Arts and crafts, I thought. I then proceeded to use the toilet paper and water to make a paper Mache sculpture; the first thing that I sculpted was a woman, of course, because I think that a woman's form is the basis for art. They are formed with nice curves in the waist and chest area, very similar to pottery, a very old form of art. The woman I crafted had large hips and breasts and on the shorter side, a very nicely shaped woman, quite beautiful, I would say. Hips are one thing I like because it shows that a woman has great childbearing potential. The next sculpture that I made was a skeleton, a symbol of life and death with a fire in between them and a yin and yang as the moon. The woman and skeleton were dancing around a fire. The yin and yang have always been very important symbols to me. It's a sign of the good and the bad, it symbolizes how the world works, people and forces need to work together because when people or forces fight, nothing will be accomplished. The yin and the yang is also the sign of a man and a woman, the dark and the light, the sun and the moon. I felt comfort in my art and I also snuck a piece of paper in that reminded me of Sarah Grafton.

The piece of paper goes way back to when I tried to ask her out one Christmas. I had hand crafted a table for her and made her a queen chess piece on my grandfather's lathe. I had sent her my other grandfather's favorite movie to her with a piece of paper inside that said that she was my universe. I had made myself the same piece of paper to remind me of her and I have carried it in my wallet ever since. For some reason, I had thought to sneak it in with me and I managed to get away with it. The paper had brought me peace through the whole experience in the same way that she used to when we were together. The whole time I was wondering what she was up to. I found it very weird as well that I had had the dream about her the night before. I wondered if maybe she was thinking about me. I always liked her because she is a strong woman and she gives me strength through the hard times, even just the thought of her helps.

The one bonus of the jail is that there were quite a few good-looking female guards around and I could always find her beauty in all of them. So, there is some positivity in this place. When I was making my toilet paper art on the desk in this very tiny room, the guard came around and saw me making additions to my sculpture and she told me to stop but I could tell by the look in her eyes that she didn't really care, with a half-smile she walked away. It was nice having the feeling of being watched over by such beauty. I had to spend two days in this cell before I was transferred to the general population, where I hoped that the food would be better and maybe a bit more freedom. When I moved over, though, nothing was different other than I realized that I liked my privacy. This is what I thought at first but after a few days to get to know the guys in the cell, it began to not be so bad other than having to learn how to sleep with a lot of noise around. Other than that, it's not so bad playing cards and socializing, but I'm still learning to cope.

There are a few people that have given me some problems but nothing I couldn't manage to ignore. Other than that, it's fun getting to know people. There are some people worth talking to who want to better themselves. But the ones who don't, I find it hard to give them any of my time, not that it's worth anything, but I try to help people when I can. I am fortunate that I have been through a lot of my problems before I got in here. I'm just here to take care of this damn warrant so I can finally be free from the Law. Then I don't have to be constantly looking over my shoulder anymore and the law won't have the upper hand.

It's been about a week now and I'm finally starting to get used to the place. A couple of Mexicans and I enjoyed playing cards about once a day. They hardly speak any English, just enough that we can communicate slightly. They are funny as hell to play cards with, they can really lift your spirits very easily. I have always liked Mexicans because no matter what, they always seem to be in good spirits and they just like to have a good time. We play a game called garbage and we work together to screw the fourth player. Well, really you can screw whoever you want but we all kind of picked on this very annoying guy in our cell. It was very entertaining, even with the language barrier there was still understanding between us, cards are kind of a universal language in a way and my favorite activity to pass the time; it really flies because you get a chance to forget the hell that we are all really in. The longer you stay in here, the more used to it you get. You learn how to have great patients. Jail is not a place to be in a hurry because nothing is done at a fast pace around here, so you might as well learn some patience and slow down. Really this is a good lesson in general, "PATIENCE IS A VIRTUE" is what they say and the more of it you have, the more at peace you will become. Life is not a race and if it is, you can go back to the story of the tortoise and the hare and it tells you who the true winner is, it's the man with wisdom and understanding, the man who takes his time is always going to be the winner.

We received commissary today, so today has been a good day. It's a good time to make someone's day as well as your own. For a group of people with nothing in here, it sure is nice to see them share food and goods with each other. It creates an opportunity for conversation and friendship. Today one of the Mexicans had powdered doughnuts as we were playing cards. There are very few in a sleeve, but he still offered one to everyone around. He gave one to the other Mexican Concho and when no one was looking, he smeared the white powder under his nose and began acting like a man strung out on cocaine. He had the powder everywhere on his face and on the table as well. He began to sniff profusely and make his eyes bulge out of his skull. It was one of the funniest things I have seen in here yet. The whole-cell burst out into a loud roar of laughter, a true highlight of the day, you don't get many of them while you're here. Just every now and then, but you learn to cherish these memories because there's not much else in here. I'm telling you, these Mexicans know how to have a good time. They don't judge you, they are the outcasts in here, like me in a way, because their language barrier is like me needing to work out my brain writing. There's not much brain stimulation in here, so I really have no one to talk to either, just like they are the only Mexicans in here that speak Spanish. Those Mexican were truly some of the best people that I had met while I was in that awful place.

In my commissary, I ordered a lot of tortillas and red beans and rice. The Mexicans were more than happy to throw down supplies for burritos, so our cell could all have a miniature kind of fiesta. Also, the coffee came in and thank God for that. It is like god damn cocaine in this place and if you drink too much of it, you will literally thwack out like you never have before. It's good to be able to share with people and it is one of the best bargaining chips here and the Raman noodle soups. It's funny how the system works here. It's kind of like the old west in here. Trade and barter and the toughest wins, but everyone here is soft, they just play the bullshit persona jail tough guy, but most of them just put on the show because everyone else does, it's funny to watch. You will get the scrawny white guy trying to talk like a gangster in front of the homies. It really is one big joke, I wish a lot of people would drop the game and then maybe I would socialize more. But to tell the truth, I thoroughly enjoy the peace and quiet when I get the opportunity. These eight-man cells make it hard sometimes to find time to get into my thoughts and relax.

16

JULY 18, MY COURT DAY AT LAST

I have been in this fucking dump now for 10 days, finally getting accustomed to the idea of the whole thing. The reason the strong survive is because they learned to adapt, that's how the world and mankind have made it this far, so I figured I better get with the program. I have court tomorrow and haven't been able to sleep all night and I'm praying for good news in the morning, we will have to see if I can get some fucking sleep.

Finally, court day at last, I managed to get a whole 3 hours of sleep before court. I decided to wake up early to do my hair and b my teeth. I had court, so I figured if I woke up for breakfast at 6:30, I would have time to get ready, but the bastards were here right at 6:30 to take me to court 4 hours early, so I got to show up really looking like a bum "PERFECT" nothing like trying to impress the judge looking like you woke up on the wrong side of the bed. My hair was a mess and I looked like an absolute madman. "AT LEAST I SHOWED UP AS MY TRUE SELF, NO BULLSHIT THIS TIME IN FRONT OF THE JUDGE." looking like the all-American bum, long-haired and dirty as hell in my best pair of jailhouse jumpers with chains around my hands and feet. "A REAL FEELING OF BEING DOOMED"

My court-appointed attorney was a real dumb bastard. I could not figure out how this man managed to get his law degree, he must have done poorly in college, being that he works for the state and doesn't have his own law firm. "FUCK" I should have just represented myself. If this man was a salesperson, I wouldn't buy shit from the man. Except maybe a tanning membership to whatever god-awful place he goes. It almost looked as bad as Donald Trump, that fake gold tan color, absolutely god-awful. He reeked of cheap cologne and wore a very cheap-looking suit poorly made. I could tell that from across the room. The bastard had a brilliant idea to lie to the court about how I left the state, not knowing that I was still on probation. Which was an absolute lie? "IT PISSED ME OFF" He told me to trust him and my heart sank. "FUCK, MY LIFE IS IN THIS BIG DUMMIE'S HANDS. I MOST CERTAINLY AM DOOMED." As he was talking to the judge, I pictured I was standing next to an orangutan and he was flailing his arms about with shit in hand, begging for a god damn bunch of bananas. This is not good behavior trying to get a treat. The judge kept asking him to perform circus tricks and he couldn't perform these simple tasks. He knew no tricks at all. I felt as if I was a circus ring leader and my paycheck depended on this bum chimp that some stranger from the street sent me to work with, telling me he would do great. Neglecting to tell me that he had a bum leg and was dumber than shit. "NO USE AT ALL" After he attempted to do his trick, the district attorney laughed and looked me straight in the eye and told me that she did not believe the story the orangutan had told, also mentioning that she did not appreciate the shit being thrown around the room. I apologized to her telling her that I found this dirty animal out on the street, but it was my only option. I then looked over at the dumb ass and stared straight at him like why the fuck did you lie in court, you useless piece of shit, they just called me out in front of the whole court for a bullshit lie. My own attorney made me look like an idiot. He sensed me glaring at him out of the corner of his eye, he knew he had fucked up. I would have just told them the truth, the bastard was in contempt of court. I'm glad that they didn't try to pin that on me, or I probably would have called him a fucking idiot right there on the spot. "FUCK MAN, I WAS READY FOR THE WRATH

OF THE JUDGE. WHY WOULD YOU MAKE UP A STOOPID LIE
LIKE THAT" He didn't even ask for the agreement that we had talked
about. We were asking for time served, but I think the judge saw me
eyeballing him about the lie, so he cut me some slack on my sentenc-
ing. Something told me that he had worked with this orangutan
before and he knew of his bum leg and nasty ways of tossing shit all
over the place and that he most certainly wasn't able to perform the
simple task of being my attorney. So, the judge stepped in to help me
out because obviously, this moron had not a single clue what he was
doing and had no respect from the courtroom at all. Who even made
this man an attorney? I don't know. Well, thank Jesus that the judge
was on my side because the district attorney wanted me to do 120
days. The judge had lowered the sentence to 50 days since I had
already served 20, so it turned out pretty good I thought He also gave
me the opportunity for work release and that my friends were the
best blessing of it all. If I qualify, I will be able to leave jail and go to a
work program where I can at least get a full-time job and only sit in
jail at night, the most ideal situation. If everything pans out, I could
possibly leave jail with possibly a thousand or two dollars in the
bank, which would help greatly in getting some of my projects
completed, preferably get my damn fifty-three Buick back on the
road. It is the road master at that. I'm ready to peak the speedometer
needle once more on that thing.

Well, it's been a few days now, almost a week has gone by fast till
today. It was a good day in the fact that the work release man came
and woke me up. It was strange because I dreamed about the man
coming and I was awoken by him coming to see me. He brought me
the good news that I had been accepted for the program and that I
should be moved to the facility within the week. After hearing the
news though, I have become restless and the day has drug on forever.
It doesn't help that the commissary comes tomorrow either and I am
starving from the lack of food they serve here. I hate these restless
nights too much time for thinking. Whenever I get like this, my
thoughts always seem to think of Sarah. I have never been able to
figure it out with her, but she has been my top girl since the day I met

her. It was back in high school and we both had detention together. I had never met her and was introduced to her by my friend Ethan. It was like something out of a movie if you have ever seen one about love at first sight. She stuttered my words. We had a brief time to get stoned before we had to go to detention after school. So, Ethan, Sarah, and I hopped into Ethan's truck and got stoned before our detention sentence. When we got back to school to sit out our time, we walked into the detention room and sat down. Sarah had to sit on the other side of the room from me, but we were facing each other. I had a hard time not smiling at her when I looked across the room. Being very high did not help this at all. There was something about her that made me want to try to get her to marry me from the first day I laid eyes on her. Still, to this day, I don't know why she returns to my mind so much or why I wrote down her number when I came in here or why I carried a little piece of paper around with me to remind me of her. Like I said, I had to sneak it in here with me and somehow got away with it in here with me. I haven't spoken to her in years, but still, I carry the damn thing around with me. I wrote her number down and have wanted to call her almost every day I have been here, but I don't want to be a disappointment to her when she gets a call from the jail, as it states my name and says that it's from the Johnson County detention center. I always wanted to be my best to her. But getting this legal stuff taken care of is a big step in improving myself. I really don't know why I felt I should call her since it has been so long ,but deep down in my heart, I felt I should call her. I know she would travel great distances if I was ever in trouble, I just know she would: if I was on my death bed, she would be there and I do the same for her. I miss her a lot and I dream about her a lot. She shows up in my dreams more than anyone else. There must be some reason I always hope that maybe she is thinking about me at that time, just maybe, or maybe it's just false hope.

17

JULY 29

I was realized from jail and sent to the work release center today. They came and got me early this morning. I slept in past breakfast because it's terrible cereal and powdered milk. It's terrible, so it's easy to sleep past the morning call. They ended up calling me about 30 minutes after the breakfast call telling me to pack my things to leave, it was a great surprise to the morning. I packed my things and gave away the last of my commissary to my fellow Bunkie's they thanked me with great pleasure on their faces and said their good bye. I was very pleased to leave. They brought me back to the property room where this whole trip to hell began where they proceeded to give me my things back, finally back in my own clothes, got my boots back on and my shirt back. I finally started to feel like my old self again, It's funny how the sight of my old work boots brought me joy after being in this place for so long. It was nice lacing up my old boots because they are so worn out that my feet fit the souls perfectly. After walking out, I was placed in an actual car with no handcuffs on or anything. Finally, a hint of freedom once again it was a good feeling as we drove out of the garage. I asked the guard driving if I could roll down the window to breathe some fresh air for the first time in 17 days. The man laughed and said that it was ok, but we would only be in the car for a minute top. I told him that I didn't care, that I just needed to breathe. It was nice getting my rights back a little. I didn't care because I at least got a couple of whiffs before arriving. It had rained the night before. The only reason I knew this was because I could see the lightning through the windows of the cell. Now, these aren't good windows, so don't get the wrong impression. They are about ten or fifteen feet above the ground no chance of looking out, but you can at least see if it's rainy or sunny out. Maybe even see the occasional cloud float by in the sky. One day I happened to catch a glimpse of a small Cessna fly by but no real sense of the outside world. It amazed me how much of your senses you lose while being locked up. As I stepped out of the car, I could instantly smell the flowers around me and the rain had helped intensify the effect. People don't really realize the senses they have till they are taken away from them for long periods of time. Most people take the sense of smell and taste for granted.

The center grounds, they look decent from the road. As you pull up, you can see a large garden, a volleyball court, and a large field with a horse shoe pit in it. As you head into the building, you really have a sense that this place could be nice, but you soon learn all your hopes and dreams of the place are about to be crushed. There is a main building where you eat, the nurse is there, and a property office. Then they have the living quarters, which really look nice from the outside, almost like a hotel, but you learn very quickly that it's not. For some reason, the doors are locked going in, but they are unlocked coming out. I think they do this to wean out the ones who are going to run. I'm not going to lie if I had much more time in this place I would be long gone, taking my chance with the law catching me.

You walk into the building, having to get patted down every time you come in and must go through a metal detector to reach the heart of the concrete jungle. After you are thoroughly abused, you must walk up a set of damp concrete stairs to your pod; there are about four pods in the place, all with around 20-30 beds in each. Once you reach your pod, there is a small living room with one TV and about 20 chairs. They look comfortable compared to the metal stools that they have in the jail. But the chairs are a complete illusion. I sat in one and it was a total disappointment. We made our way up to the room, as they opened the door, I thought oh hell, as the only things in there were two metal bunkbeds and four metal cabinets and one loan chair. Luckily, at least the bed mats were about an inch and a half instead of an inch. "FUCK" all I wanted to do is write and there's no fucking desk.

There still isn't a whole lot of freedom in the work release program, but you do at least get the opportunity to walk around freely inside the building between your room and the living room. The guards and the inmates are a little laxer here as well. I think a little bit of freedom gained helps the inmates start to appreciate their freedom a little more, so they try harder to maintain the freedom given to them. They are much more social than in jail, trying to lend a hand whenever they can. People are even less hostile over here, not so much of the bullshit either that everyone tries to put on in the jail. Over there, it seemed to be some sort of pride thing and it was starting to drive me mad by the time I left, but I managed to maintain composure without stealing any of their souls, just a few for good measure and a few small verbal arguments.

I was very fortunate that there was a very good-looking guard. She was beautiful and helped me stay relaxed throughout my stay. She checked me into the place and I had to try very hard to keep myself from checking her out. The female guards are funny because the laws of attraction are still there even though I am an inmate and they are in charge. I could feel her presence strongly and she looked over and we locked eyes almost like old friends lost in time. Our stare seemed to last almost a full minute before one of us looked away; she looked very good in her uniform, I could make out the shape of her body in my mind even though the uniform was rather baggie. She wasn't very tall, maybe 5 feet or so, she was small, but she was fierce, I could just tell by her presence. Something about a woman in uniform excites me, I think it's because I like to go after strong women. I'm just glad there are women guards here. They can really brighten the day, I look forward to seeing her around.

We can have a few of our belongings in here. I had a few sets of clothes and luckily, I got some paper as soon as I showed up, so I could get to writing. I soon figured out that there was in fact a desk in the room: the lockers we were given had a hidden pull-out one built in. I thought about seeing if I could have my typewriter. I decided to ask and was shut down very quickly. "BASTARDS" there is no reason why I couldn't have it there, the only regulations were two electronics, and the typewriter I use is a 1946 mechanical type. It was time to have my first meal in the place and I was excited I was told that the food was pretty good and that they had vending machines as well with soda and what not. I got to the cafeteria and to my surprise, they had beans and corn bread, one of my favorites, the others seemed a little disappointed, but to me this was a blessing, it reminded me of my grandma and grandpa's house when she used to cook them up for me and I would eat them for a week straight. The funny thing is that when I was in jail, all I asked for was some beans and cornbread over there. It was absolute hell because they said they were remodeling their kitchen, so we were fed bologna sandwiches almost every meal. They had a few different things, but it was basically a sack lunch. I'm curious if they heard my request for the beans and cornbread and they had the kitchen cook them up just for me when I showed up.

18

AUGUST 8

It's Friday. I have been in this goddamn place since Monday, the whole point of this place is to help you get to work. It seems as if they try to slow you down as much as possible around every corner. I was supposed to leave today to go pick up applications, but I was hoping to double task and get my lawn mowing business back afloat, but when it was about that time to leave, I went down to the property office to ask if I could get my phone for the day. They told me that I had to fill out a special paper form to receive it. The property lady damn well could have just given me my phone and the paper to fill out right there on the spot, but no, that would be too easy for them to do that and way too convenient for someone locked up. She just insisted on being a bitch about the whole thing. These guards here are funny, some of them hate their jobs so much, which I find easy to believe since they are literally going to jail for their money. Yeah, they are not getting physically locked in like I am, but they still sit behind the same walls. Hell, even on the outs, people go to jail for their jobs and have no problem doing so, or there just too scared to do anything about it. The funny thing is these guards that are pricks and are rude, living just as miserable of a life on the outs as I am living here. So, they take that out on us or on their children at home, it's a crying shame how some people act. It's a sickening thing to watch. I hate to see people so miserable that they put their bad and hate towards other people. Luckily not all the guards are this way. They understand that it is a shit show in here. Your attitude towards them also plays a big role in how they treat you. A lot of these other inmates don't understand that either. To me, they are the real fools. "TREAT PEOPLE THE WAY THAT YOU WOULD LIKE TO BE TREATED" that's a good rule of thumb.

Back about three years ago, I placed myself in a drug rehab facility because I was tired of being on rock bottom. They sat the whole class down and they told us that the program only had a five percent success rating. I got to thinking to myself why you would tell these people that— are leaving no hope in the people left there. But after a while, I thought about it and me being the person that I am, I took that as a challenge. Really it helped me in the long road because I fought to better myself just to prove the fuckers wrong. More people need to have this kind of mindset, we would have a tougher generation. I feel like here in jail, it's about the same percentage rating, maybe a little higher though "BUT NOT MUCH" I have seen a few faces which I think will leave this place and not come back. There's plenty more though, that I see right back here "VERY SOON" because of pure stupidity. They have no will to improve.

I had this roommate, Pat, that just left today. He seemed like a good kid, he was 19 and he said he had spent the last few years in custody for different things. He was leaving after a year's stay. I wish the kid the best of luck. I have a strange feeling that he won't make it too long. The night before, he was talking to another roommate about getting high and I told the kid what it took me to get sober and that I had to get away from all that shit and how I kept myself away from people for two years to finally be able to cope. I told him once I stopped paying for drugs. I have things to show my improvements today. I see multiple cars in the driveway, a motorcycle and owning two different boats. In the last few years, I have truly been playing the game of life. I don't have to look behind my back anymore. Once I leave this place, I am a free man once more. I haven't been free from the law for many years. I'm excited to finally do what I please. I feel bad for Pat because he grew up in the system. H didn't know any better than these "DUMB FUCKS" he has been around the last few years. I really do hope the best for the kid, maybe the kid will have a chance!!! "THE KID DESERVES A CHANCE" He just needs to avoid the drugs till he has made something for himself. I thought if you have your life going well it's ok to treat yourself every now and again. "JUST DONT LET ANYTHING TAKE AHOLD OF YOU" I wish other people in here would see it that way. I think that's a false hope, though. They just want to fuck off and just wait for the day they can get high again and do the same stupid shit that got them in here in the first place. At least I had a few years of getting my ducks in a row. I came back, and it wasn't for fucking up with drugs. Just a damn speeding ticket and getting picked up on a warrant from over four years ago. I came in this time with a vengeance knowing that the fuckers didn't have shit on me anymore. They try to break you down in here and the best defense is not letting them get to you. You must show them that you are better than that petty shit they try to make you feel bad for. You just must wait till they don't have any more ammunition.

19

AUGUST 2

I have been getting some work lined up with this work-release program. I applied for a job with a metal fabricating company and have been waiting a few days to hear back from them, but still no response. I also applied for a lawn mowing job that I should have in the bag, but I have been taking care of some personal issues like getting my ID and driver's license back. When I get out of here, I'm probably going to quit whatever job I get to go back to doing my own business. So, I'm trying to do things that can help with life once I leave this place. It should be nice to have my license back after not having one for about 5 years. Today I went outside for recreation to play some horseshoes. It's been a daily activity since I have been here. One of the guards came out to watch us play. I started a conversation with the man by asking him if he would like to play. He informed me that they would string him up and fire him if he was to throw one horseshoe. I thought this was completely absurd. "HE AGREED" he then began to tell me that he wasn't even allowed to smoke in the inmates' smoking area. I asked him why he decided to be a guard he told me that he didn't know. He said he disliked the job. I asked him why he would want to go to jail for his job. Sounds like it's "PRETTY SHIT". The guard began telling me that he had served in the military

154

for six years prior of being a jail guard. I thanked the man for his service like I always do when I meet a veteran. He was telling me about his time in Afghanistan, riding in Humvees and eventually becoming a part of a tank crew. I asked him if he had ever seen any combat, he told me a time that his Humvee was being fired upon and all you could hear were bullets ricocheting off the side of the truck. I then told him if I was in the military, I would have liked to be in WW1 or 2 where there was close combat and blood and gore. He looked at me kind of funny when I said that, but I think he agreed with me. He said it would be tough watching friends fall and I felt his dilemma, I then said that should be the drive to fight harder. I started asking him about the modern military equipment and what he thought about it and if it was easy to work on. He told me all the equipment they use today is very easy to repair, telling me that they could swap the turbine engine out of a tank in a matter of hours to get it back in the field. The facility was right next door to a military base and I began to ask him about the Humvees; he then told me how easy it would be to steal one of them from the base, he said they didn't even keep the keys in them and when they are stored like that all they have is a simple padlock on the doors he said nothing that a good pair of bolt cutters wouldn't take care of. Other than that, he said there is a glow plug switch that you have to kick on for about 60 seconds before you start the thing. This all made me laugh because I had thought about trying to steal one the day before, wondering what kind of effort it would take. Then literally, this guard walks up to me the next day, telling me how simple it would be without me even asking.

Since I have been in jail, I started writing again and finishing up on my current book that I have been working on for a little more than a year. I wish I had a place to write other than jail. I always pictured writing on a beach with the waves crashing in the background with a nice sunset. Maybe have a small beach house, or maybe just have a large boat to live on. A relaxing place where ever it is, possibly even a place in the mountains somewhere like Hunter S Thompson's place at owl farm, a place to escape from the monotony of it all, possibly even both mountains in the summer and the beach in the winter. I think I have decided though, that I want to write for a living or at least give it a try with this first book. Like most writers, though, you must fail a few times but keep writing. I have a very good feeling about my work though it's all about getting it in the right hands. Shit, the world could use a good fucking movie. I have an original story, at least one that hasn't been seen before, so if they like it, they can make a new goddamn movie instead of ruining the classics by trying to remake them. The only thing that I ask is that they don't use the goddamn green screens and put the characters in real locations. I don't want any phoniness in the films. Fuck I wrote the story by having to live it, so don't trash my work by using stupid green screens and cheap movie effects. I know this might just be a wild pipe dream, but it's one I decided to pursue. Someday I picture myself in a peaceful place making money off one of my books, sipping a double jack on the rocks watching my wife laid beside me comfortably while I sit back and write, with no worries in the world. There are only two things I lack about, this fantasy and that is a peaceful place and a wife. At least I have worked on my boat all summer, so as soon as I get out of this hell of a place, I'll escape for a month or so on the boat and finally get to relax. It's funny to me how jail can change a man if you let it. It's good for some if they really want change, but for the ones who don't, they will return time and time again. There is a certain lesson you need to learn, but you must search yourself to do so. You also can't let the place break you, you must conform to it, but dammit, do not let them break you. If you have good values deep within, keep your faith in it and don't let the system take them from you like some of these dummies in here and when you're free "GET OUT AND LIVE".

"Life is not a journey to the grave with the intention of arriving safely in a pretty and well-preserved body. But rather, to skid in broadside, thoroughly used up, totally worn out, and loudly proclaiming... WOW
what a ride."
Hunter S. Thompson

Today was a decent day. I managed to get a job at a restaurant called Houlihan's. I don't know how well I'm going to like the job because I have been working for myself for the last few years. I only must work for Houlihan's because the center I'm at won't let me pursue my own career. They say they want to help these inmates, but almost all my business I have worked for, they have tried to destroy. I have lost my lawn care business because they won't let me call my customers, I managed to talk to a few of them and they said that they would like me back when I'm out. I had big plans to have my most successful year yet after changing my ways from hard drugs. I was going to sell my boat for a year's salary, but I am running out of summer to do so. The boat was my breakthrough to start my own business for real. I am very happy about the job at Houlihan's, though, because I get to leave the center "THANK GOD FOR THAT MAN" and thank God for the beautiful women who work there. Women are always my escape, I can leave the world when I'm around them. I wish I could take them with me on my mental journeys. I often imagine being on my boat with them. I sat waiting for my orientation and I dreamed of going out on my boat with one of them or multiple of them. There is a very cute redhead who just started about a week ago. I watched her folding napkins. She looked so elegant while she did this simple task. I drifted off to my boat and I could picture her in a bikini getting some sun, she is very beautiful. There is something about a red head that intrigues me. She seemed a little uneasy with herself for some reason, especially when her coworker came to help with her chore. The other girl was a blonde, she was very beautiful as well, but I could tell the redhead felt uneasy around her, which I could not understand. She was just as beautiful as the blonde, when I look at women, I find beauty in all of them. I'm looking forward to getting a chance to meet these girls. I then pictured them both in bikinis on the boat. It was a wild fantasy, there was also a taller blonde; she too was just as beautiful as the rest of them, all the girls carried supreme elegance about them. It should be nice to meet some girls not in a bar for once. I have really hidden myself away in my work, not really getting out much, so the job should be good for me. I really like the general manager as well, she is a very curvy woman, and she is full of spunk and gives off a feeling of comfort around her. She always has a smile on her face and a positive attitude about her, I bet it's because she is stoned all the time, but who cares? That's what makes her nice.

It's a rare thing anymore "TRUE FREEDOM" many people try to find it but not too many people succeed.

I have found it a few times in life "TRUE FREEDOM" but as I go through time, I find that glimpse of hope in women. It's like a chance to get out of my skin and a chance for true love and adventure. I hope to share it while I can, "HELL" who knows how much time I have left on this spinning ball in space and time. I just want to share my love and passion. I feel if a good woman wanted to take a chance, we could have great adventures, even if it was just a fling, it would be one to remember. I just want to share stories and travels to help write a story of good to maybe help mankind. I feel like anymore the media and TV show violence and it sickens me to the core. Deep down, I'm full of love. This woman gave me a job and I feel as if I can learn some things from her. She has a very big heart and she can see that I still have a heart even though I feel it fading every day. I must fight hard every day to keep a good heart and that's where the women truly help me. Sometimes I feel as if I'm dying inside and somehow, I feel the girls feel the same way, just trying to get by and trying to find something more in life than work and being slaves to the bullshit that we call life. Anymore, in the eyes of them all, I can see a glimpse of hope that there's something better for us out there. I feel like they still see a glimpse of hope left in me even though I feel life is "DOOMED" I still try, though, to find the beauty around and want to share what I have worked for with them and give them a chance to escape and find true freedom once again, that feeling of being a child and no care in the world the one that the man wants to rob us from every day. I'm glad that people can see that, and if the man wants to try and bring me or any of my friends down, then bring it on. I will fight to the teeth to keep that from happening. The world is a cruel place these days and I refuse to be taken down by the swine that make it that way. I must continue to try and inspire others and do my best. "LOVE THE HATERS AND THEY WILL GET WHAT'S COMING TO THEM IN GOOD TIME" I will not have any worries anymore. I look around this life and I see a bunch of strong people. They could be great, but they have been lost for so long they don't know any better. I see this all over. It's the sad truth of this world, they don't know any better, so they don't fight for it. I guess it's hard to fight for something that you don't know exists.

I saw a man today during his visitation, his wife had brought his daughters to see him and I watched as his wife watched her husband enjoying the company of his kids. This brought joy to me to see that kind of love. They were just playing a board game together. It reminded me of a time when my son was very young, him not knowing that I was his father. We got to play like children. Me being about 20 and him about 7, we played cops and robbers on a wood train set playground that he had. For that moment in time, I got to truly feel young again, I didn't see him much, but it was a few years later and he still remembers that moment in time, when I asked him about it. I would like to enjoy more time like that, I have felt robbed of the feeling of being a father and more importantly, he has been robbed of his father, partially my fault but also his uncle's fault, who adopted him for not wanting me to spend time with him, telling me that he didn't have time to spend time with me because of school. But if the kid still remembers that time on the playset for an hour tops four years later, I think of all the memories that could have been that he has lost, neglected from spending time with his own father. His mother passed away last year, so he will never get that time with her now. My uncle said that he is too busy to be with his own father, so if I was to die tomorrow, the kid would never have the chance to know his real parents. He will only know about the time on the playground and my story if he ever gets to read it. To me, this is a crime, just as if the man in the visitation room couldn't see his daughters. To rob a child from his or her true roots. An hour or twos time a day could make a huge difference in the growth of a child and should not be neglected.

"I DON'T KNOW HOW MANY YEARS I HAVE LEFT IN THIS WORLD, BUT I'M GOING TO GET REAL WEIRD WITH IT"

20

AUGUST 12

It's been two weeks in the work release program this past week, I have started work. I managed to get four days in this week and about 28 hours. I'm only making a measly 300 dollars. I have at least made enough to get even with the place on the money that I owe. The last few days of work have been great. Finally getting to meet new people, one who stands out more than most is a girl named Megan. She's only nineteen but my, how she glows when she's around. She's blonde with curly hair and a very cute face. She's about my height and very well put together, with an almost perfect hourglass-shaped body and lightly toned skin. She is young but puts off as being much older. I would have given her around 25 for her maturity. My oh my, how she lights up the room. She didn't work the weekends, but I was missing her when she wasn't there, I had only talked to her for a couple of days, but I grew an attraction to her during the two days. I was washing dishes at the restaurant and she would come back and help every now and again, even though she was a server. I felt like she would come back to the dish room just to flirt. I thoroughly enjoyed seeing her wash the dishes. She would look over with a cute smile and I could see her nose piercing, she looked amazing. I plan on trying to talk to her more. I possibly even asked her out on a date when I got out of the center. I talked to her about going out on my boat and she said that it sounded nice she began telling me how she could use a good vacation. I agreed with her telling her I was taking one as soon as I got out of this goddamn jail.

Today I was told that I must go to another location Houlihan's, for training on how to do the dishes. I thought to myself, "WHAT THE HELL" these bastards hired me for a week and I have already been doing the dishes, what could they possibly train me on at this new place. They said that I had to go on my first day at the new location. I figured out that there was no training at all. They just needed help because they were short-staffed. I don't know what my manager told them from the other store, but when I showed up, I had to learn the new layout, which wasn't bad other than the whole place was completely opposite, the washing machine was switched from left to right, so the muscle movements were completely flipped. I also had many more names to remember after working so hard to remember names from the other location. Again, though there were plenty of beautiful women to keep me calm, so I felt comfort in this new place. They were being short-staffed and me being the only dishwasher, I had to make up for the work of two. It was a bit overwhelming but nothing that I couldn't handle. The dishes stacked up higher and higher. I thought the fucking things were going to stack up clear to the sky. At that point, I was considering walking right out of place, telling them that I quit for bad conditions and lack of drive to wash fucking dishes. At that point, I remembered the bastards had me right where they wanted me. I couldn't just quit the job because it would have been against the jail's contract. I had to maintain this job for 30 days, so I wouldn't have to go back to jail. The dishes were now beginning to block the doorway, where I couldn't even leave the dish room to put the clean ones away. I buckled down and kept at it. I could feel the whole staff watching me, just waiting for me to break. Waiting for the moment that I would fail, but the bastards don't know who they were messing with or the hell that I had been through. I pushed through till the end. It was about one in the morning when I was about done; at that point, I could tell the kitchen staff wanted to help me finish, but the bastard managers wanted to try and break me to see if I was worthwhile. I proved them all wrong. I took the challenge and conquered it. The worst part of the whole thing is that I have worked hard the last three years building my own business, so I wouldn't have to do this line of work. The monotony of it all can and will take a toll on a man if they are not strong enough to handle the stresses. The next few days showed me proof of this. Listening to other employees talk about the Deja Vu that a job like this makes you feel. This feeling of being doomed in a job like this was, in fact, the drive that pushed me to better myself and start doing my own work.

"I have no taste for either poverty or honest labor, so writing is the only recourse left for me."
Hunter S. Thompson

In the path I have taken, I get more stimulation, I prefer to keep my mind alive rather than let the man shut off my brain like the sheep they like to train. I will always be a wolf in this country of sheep, the lone desperado fighting for broader horizons and fuller life.
Patrick McAuley

After I had gotten off work from the hellacious day, I had to wait for the damn bus to pick me up. It was pouring rain, a total downpour, of course. I had to walk to the bus stop, luckily the rain had let up long enough for me to walk the half mile or so to the bus stop. Before I left, I grabbed a trash bag to use as a poncho if the rain got bad but luckily, I didn't have to use it. As I was getting close to the stop, the rain began to worsen. I ran the last block to try and beat the storm. I managed to make it with no worse than some wet hair. It was around one thirty in the morning. The lightning show that night was constant fierce bolts shooting across the sky. None of them seemed to hit the ground though, they just ripped across the sky horizontal to the horizon, it looked as if they were shooting a couple of miles sideways in either direction. It was truly a beautiful spectacle to get to witness. The bus finally arrived to pick me up. Soon to be one of the worst bus rides yet. It was now about one forty-five, I was the first passenger on the route. The bus came screeching into the parking lot, looking like the driver was doing about sixty-five as he whipped the van around the corner in

the pouring rain. The driver I knew well by this point was a goofy younger guard, but he meant well. The man drives like a complete maniac, though. For some reason, I took comfort in that because it reminded me of some of my driving skills, but I never drive in this manner with passengers with me. We hit the highway and the man seemed to not care at all about the weather conditions. The buses are equipped with seatbelts which I had neglected to wear till this trip. These are ford conversion vans with a high-top roof. They have one major flaw ford neglected to notice. It gave me the urge to write them personally about the flaw in their design. The problem is that when driving in heavy rain, the water whisking off the tires pelts the inside of the wheel wells with a savage roar. It sounds like you are power-washing a large piece of sheet metal. The racket was terrible, so loud that you could hardly hear your own thoughts. We finally got off the highway and the sound finally dampened, we had a long route that night, having to pick up ten or twelve more people, as we got further through the route. The driver was calling into the center on his radio, neglecting to see the bright red light in front of him. Blowing right through the intersection at top speed "DEAR LORD, THIS MIGHT BE MY LAST RIDE EVER" the funny thing is, this wouldn't be my last time thinking this on this trip. We were nearing the end of the route the bus was about full. There was a god-awful smell in the thing now of body odor and burnt cigarettes. We neared the exit to go back to the jail and the driver flew right past it, not even glaring at the sign or anything. There were only two more seats left on the bus. The time was now nearing about three in the morning. I was feeling rather worn out at this point. We got further and further past the exit. I could not figure out where we were headed. We had gone about five or ten miles past the exit. We got off at an exit that seemed like the middle of nowhere.

I had a brief thought to myself that this was, in fact, the end. The bastard driver had a bus full of degenerates, me being one of them. He was taking the whole lot of us out in the middle of nowhere. To some field where we would stand in front of a firing squad and be forced to dig our own mass grave in the muck of it all after the hard rain and one by one must stand in front of the firing squad. "I CAME TO THE CONCLUSION THAT THIS WAS THE END OF THE ROAD" If this is the case, I guess I might as well volunteer myself to go first and just get the thing over with. We then got off the paved road and onto gravel, bringing my fear to reality. "FUCK, I THOUGHT" what if we really are headed to our "DOOM" I looked around, wondering if anyone else was picking up this vibe. Everyone seemed oblivious to it all. They were all on their phones, like the normal people of society,not paying attention to anything. These phones and video games today are like blinders on a horse to lower the risk of them all getting spooked by traffic, keeping the beasts from a complete panic and freak out. Without them, the carriage would run wildly out of control, the driver jumping to safety, dropping the rains after not being able to regain control of the beasts as they run down the sidewalk trampling innocent bystanders. It really is allotting like people on their phones. The people are blind to everything, glued to their screens, like bugs mesmerized by a large bug zapper swarming closer and closer till the thing gives them the best high voltage shock of their life that would most certainly be their last. But the bright lights and everything draw them closer. We eventually topped the hill, where we saw the lights of a loan factory in the distance. I finally had a sense of relief, knowing we weren't going to the mass grave that I had pictured. A sad part of me wished that I did go through to escape the monotony of it all. "NOT TODAY, SATAN" we picked up the last two riders and began the terrible packed trip on the bus back to the jail. God, we all looked terrible by the end of the ordeal, all worn out, almost to our breaking point.

This job is starting to get to me. I'm really getting tired of working so hard for peanuts after working so hard the past few years to not have to do so. I just worked a double yesterday starting at eight thirty, working till four, and then hopping to the other location at five, working till about one in the morning. Yet again, I had to get on the god damn bus, not getting back till three thirty at night once again. I then had to catch the next bus at five, only two hours to try and sleep. When I told them I needed to catch the next bus in two hours, they then informed me that I had to stay at the center for eight hours till I could leave. I had known this, but I played dumb, telling them that it was complete bullshit that they were doing this to me. I then came up with a bullshit story about how I would get fired if I did not show up. Which was a lie, but I had to be convincing to fool the dummies working at the center. With a little convincing, I managed to get them to let me leave even though it was against court orders to let me do so. I had the bastard's right where I wanted them as I had called in the night before to cover my ass, telling them that they had given me permission the night before, knowing damn well that I had done the scam on purpose. I had got the best of them for the first time since I had been locked up. The next day was complete hell, only getting about an hour of sleep before going back to work. Luckily there was a Starbucks next to work, so I managed to get a cup of Joe at least. It really didn't cut it. What I did crave though, was a glass of whiskey, the perfect cure to a night with no sleep. I had a minor hallucination that morning when a coworker asked me for a wire whisk under the counter. In my ears, I heard hand me the whisky fifth down there. I thought for a second, "SHIT, THEY KEEP A BOTTLE OF WHISKEY DOWN HERE. GOOD DEAL" but it was just my sleepless mind playing tricks.

The day was going to be hell; I had hoped Megan would be in

since I hadn't seen her on Monday after the transfer to the other store for the week. I thought about the girl a lot, I barely knew her, but she had a certain elegance she carried around. The age difference between us didn't seem to bother her. I was only eight years older, so that was that big of a difference. She lifts my spirits when she's around. I overheard her talking to a fellow employee that she wasn't a young flower anymore, but she truly is in my eyes. For some reason, I pictured myself teaching her how to ride my motorcycle. She's young enough, I think she still holds that innocence and fun-seeking spirit willing to try new things. I wonder if she has even been around a motorcycle.

Today I tried to initiate a conversation with her, but her sheer beauty stutters my words. I wish that I wasn't locked up, otherwise I would ask her out soon, but with my predicament, what was I supposed to do? Maybe have her come visit me in jail, just the thought of that cracked me up. Hell, I would feel like the king of the place if a cute thing like herself came to visit jail. It's worse than high school in here, the news would spread like wildfire, that a woman of such caliber and beauty came to visit me. I don't know how I could keep myself from pulling her hourglass figure close to me, clinching her firmly around the waist. Dear God, how beautiful this girl is, everything about her is perfect. I can't find a single flaw. I imagine a fierce scene of fierce kissing and a great sex scene right on the table in front of the other inmates. Their wives just wishing that their husbands had the same fierce desires as we would have shown. As of now, I'm just glad to have a woman of great beauty around work to help keep my sanity. My mind is too complex for doing the dishes all day, the women of the place are the only thingsstimulating about the whole job. The other day I sat eating a salmon Caesar salad. There were a few other servers sitting at the table next to me in a small group. Kind of like the red hat ladies if you have ever seen them before, they meet at random restaurants and they all wear red hats and talk about God knows what, as I sat and watched them and observed their conversation. I could hear them talking about ordering all the deserts that the restaurant had. The girls were fantasizing about devouring all the sweets the place had to offer. They say you can win the heart of a woman with sweets. You just must limit the amount that you give her, so you don't wake up to Free Willy, unless you're into that kind of thing. If you are, I heard that you butter up behind their fat right behind their knee and fuck her leg, it is considered a great delicacy in certain circles. Megan was talking to Emma, the manager, about ordering all the deserts on the menu and walked over to the register, where she pulled a ten-foot-long ticket out of the register where Emma was standing. "FUCK, I THOUGHT THEY REALLY DID ORDER EVERYTHING" I yelled across the table at Megan, asking if she really did order everything and she laughed and said she was just printing off the day's tabs. I said thank God to myself, knowing she wasn't destroying the beautiful figure that she had. I then pictured the both of us older gorging ourselves on plates of cake in a fancy restaurant. If the only thing that the red-hatted ladies talked about was ordering all the deserts and not a mass takeover of the world by older mediocre red-hatted women, then I'm ok with them. Those red-hatted ladies always seemed to give me the creeps. Megan had told me that she decided not to work the night shift and I was thoroughly bummed as she left for the day. The place just doesn't feel right when she's not around.

Houlihan's is a high-stress place "I CAN SENCE IT" from fellow employees. I'm wired in the way that I can catch other people's vibes and this restaurant stresses me out. Like I said though, Megan helps greatly as well as a few of the other girls working. I can get lost in them very easily. It's nice having an escape. The other day the dishes were getting stacked up again, but the funny thing is I really didn't notice as there were two shorter girls working, both beautiful girls with large breasts. Their height is an issue when it comes to putting the glasses up on the shelf. the dishes go down low on the counter down low with a view between the shelves, but I have learned the servers as they come by from their breasts and their asses because that's all I see most of the time, but Cassidy and grace are the shorter girls with the large tracks of land. It's very hard to focus on anything as they hop on their tippy-toes to put the glasses up on the shelf.

Their breasts bouncing with every hop, I must work hard to try not to drool all over myself. Luckily grace had a low-cut shirt on and her breasts were almost popping out of her shirt and bra almost every time she put glasses up "GOOD LORD TAKE ME NOW" I thought to myself. My favorite by far, though was Megan; she was slightly taller, so when she came around, I could see her ass which is phenomenal. She too has great breasts, but her being slightly taller, I can't see her breasts bounce, but dear lord, how I would like to. Often, I move a glass rack from the top shelf so that I can see the girls come by, which makes it a lot easier to start conversations and makes it more enjoyable to wash dishes. Always trying to stop Megan every chance that I get.

I went to work today not feeling too good about the day and for a good reason too. Right off the bat, the drains in the dish room began to flood the whole floor as well as the area the servers brought the dishes was underwater. It was like a fucking swamp suddenly as the drains backed up. I rushed around the dish room, turning everything off that had water going to the drain system. I managed to not flood the whole place by doing so. I went and informed the manager and she informed me that she was calling a plumber to look. I went back to the dish room and the drains had removed some of the water. After a few minutes, the floors had drained completely "GOOD DEAL" I thought I could finally get back to work. I began to get back to work when the dishwasher had run out of soap. I went to the backroom to get more for the machine. I opened the closet to get more soap and there was none to be found. I dug around, looking everywhere and nothing. I went to the manager again, who at this point, was getting irritated with the constant questions. I told her the problem of not having soap and asked her if I could still run dishes through with just water. Letting her know that I had mountains of disses piling up, she told me we could not do any more dishes without soap. "HOLY HELL, HOW COULD THIS DAY GET ANY WORSE" The other manager told me that he would drive to the other store to get more soap and that he would be back in 22 minutes. I asked him if he was positive about the 22 minutes with some sarcasm in my voice, he didn't seem to pick up on it. He was adamant, though that would be the time that it would take, so now I had to wait, watching my job getting harder and harder as the dishes piled up. I stepped up front to talk to a few of the servers about all the problems I was having. Finally, the man got back with the soap, so I could finally get back to work. I got about ten minutes in before the god damn plumber showed up "FUCK" I raced to get as many of the dishes are done before the plumber worked his way to the drain in the dish room. I didn't manage to get much done. He showed up with his pipe snake machine, but again, progress came to a halt. The plumber reminded me of the janitor from the breakfast club. He asked me about the problem, and then I asked him if he liked his job. He told me that "IT PAYS THE MORGAGE" I agreed with him, telling him that my job sucks ass and I disliked it too. The man seemed a bit like me and I took comfort in that I don't run into many freaks like myself out there. He began telling me that the man had us all right where he wanted us all slaves to this bullshit that we call life. I looked at the man and said "SHIT, MAN YOU MUST REALLY KNOW IT ALL" he chuckled, saying that he didn't think so. I think he knew that I was being sarcastic. I told him "FUCK MAN, IT'S NOT THAT BAD, YOU KNOW, WORKING FOR PEANUTS" he looked at me puzzled. I said "YEAH MAN WORKING OURSELVES TO THE BONE FOR PEANUTS, YA KNOW, PEANUTS ARE GOOD FOR YOU MAN" he was beginning to come around to my sense of humor, agreeing that yeah, peanuts aren't so bad he then said "

YEAH, BUT ALITTLE MONEY WOULDN'T HURT EVERY NOW AND THEN EITHER" I said "SHIT, MAN I WOULDN'T BE EXPECTING ANY OF THAT ANYTIME SOON." "THE BASTARDS DON'T WANT US TO HAVE ANY OF THAT, THAT WOULD MEAN GIVING US A PIECE OF FREEDOM AND THAT'S THE LAST THING THE MAN WANTS TO GIVE OUT IS FREEDOM." "ESPECIALLY NOT IN AMERICA, THE LAND OF THE FREE" he laughed and said "YEAH YOU'RE PROBABLY RIGHT" I told him that "WE WILL GET THE BASTARDS SOMEDAY JUST BE PATIENT" but don't keep your hopes up too much or if you do be prepared to have your hopes crushed because if there's one thing the man likes more than money is crushing peoples dreams. I told him that I was out to make a new American dream again, so once again, we would have something to look forward to. I said "THE U.S. IS LOOKING PRETTY BLEEK THESE DAYS, NOT MUCH EXCITE-MENT ANYMORE AT ALL"

21

AUGUST 22

"**G**OD, I HATE MY DAYS OFF IN THIS DUMP" there's not much to do around this place. I was glad to have yesterday off because I worked three straight shifts in a row, only getting a few hours of sleep, so I needed yesterday for rest, sleeping till about three in the afternoon. Today I managed to sleep again till about three, just trying to sleep my time off. The worst part about having days off in here is that I must eat their food. I have felt a little like the mob bosses in one of those gangster movies where they get to eat like kings in jail instead of the 20 different types of slop that they feed you in here. The only thing there is to look forward to in here, is that they have a half dozen vending machines where you can at least get a soda and a candy bar and if you're lucky, one of the cute guards will be working the cafeteria. Today at least, there was one of my favorite guards working. She is very full-figured with beautiful eyes, ones that almost steal your soul from you. As I sat eating, I was having a daydream of the guard wearing one of those high hip bathing suits and her large breasts popping out of her top. For some reason, she was drinking Guinness, one of my favorite beers. She began to pour the beer right between her large breasts like a beer waterfall, the cold beer on her skin was giving her goosebumps and making her nipples rock hard. I then pictured myself getting under the crease of her breasts and chugging the beer as it cascaded between them. At that moment, my roommate came and sat down, completely ruining my daydream about the beautiful guard. I called him a bastard as he sat down, and he looked confused. I mentioned the vending machines earlier. Well, we are not allowed to have any food in our rooms and they pat us down after every meal. My roommate Bow and I devised a smuggling plan to sneak goods in for us to have in our rooms. It worked every time my dad had brought me some boxer briefs when I first came here, and I don't wear underwear, I prefer to free ball. I hate having my balls all in a bunch, but that's beyond the point. Anyway, they have a pocket in the crotch of the things and I gave Bow two pairs of them in exchange for smuggling me goods back to the room. I would have normally done this myself, but they were onto me for some reason and checked me well, but Bow didn't seem to give a fuck, they would search him and never find a thing, even though he had items almost every time. I had tried once, but I didn't even hide my stuff, I just put it right in my pocket just to see if I could walk by, they found my stuff and tried to throw it away, but I convinced the guards to let me eat my stuff telling them that I had bought it and I did not want them to take my property. For a while, Bow worked just because I gave him the boxers, but after a while, I offered to buy him things to keep smuggling for me, so we always had the room well stalked with candy and miscellaneous goods. It was frowned upon, but there wasn't much penalty for the offense. I wouldn't have to worry though, because I never did any of the dirty work. I had no worries about getting into trouble. Like I said though, I only eat the food here when I absolutely have to because I eat very well at work, usually having salmon steak salads, stuffed chicken breasts, pot roast and many more good dishes. The food is great. But when I'm forced to eat this shitty food, you win some and you lose some, I guess. Luckily, I have only had a week left and have managed to eat well. With such little time left, I figured that time would fly by, but it seems like as I get closer to getting out, the longer and longer the days get. I'm really looking forward to getting out of

this hell hole once and for all. I can almost smell the lake now and
the smell of rich mahogany.

22

AUGUST 23

I woke early for work, around five in the morning. I had to catch the bus at six. I needed to walk to the gas station for cigarettes. It's about a mile from where the bus drops me off. It was a brisk morning with a slight fog on the horizon. It's getting close to September, so we are starting to have some cool weather. I started walking and the sun began breaking the horizon. I was walking through a semi-developed part of town with newer developments. Not all the land was built on, yet there are still a few patches of land with the field still. It reminded me of my yearly dove hunt that I usually go to, which I missed this year because of this damn place. The fog and the atmosphere just felt like one of those early morning hunts. The morning was beautiful, the conditions were perfect. I finally had the feeling of being free once again after being locked up for almost two months. There was a little tree line in this empty field with a lone tree out in the middle of it. It seemed like a good place to sit that morning. The field was full of different types of different wild-flowers. It was a very tranquil spot, I wish I would have stayed there for the rest of the day, but that wasn't the case, I had to work once again. I really hate the monotony of a regular job, it's a harsh Deja Vu every morning stuck in repetition. Luckily, I had about an hour before I had to go to work, so I decided to stop in the local Starbucks in the area for a coffee and a chance to sit and relax, a true sense of freedom. I hate being locked up because I normally carry cash on me and I only had money on my card. I looked in the tip jar and it was barren of any tips. I normally like to leave at least a dollar tip whenever I can. I swiped my card and there wasn't even the option to leave a tip. I felt terrible looking at the empty tip jar. I guess that's the way of the world anymore. No way to tip without cash, I feel like I'm one of the few people who even carry cash anymore. It works a lot better most of the time for me. For instance, when I go to my local bar, I don't even have to give them my card to drink because they know I am good for it. Many times, this has helped me because I always make sure to tip generously. A few times, I have left my tab without paying on accident and asked to make it up the next time that I came in and they told me "WHAT TAB." I think it's because I walked in and told them the truth of my situation and the generous tips I normally give out. So, they let me slide. Working in the food industry lately, I have discovered that there are a lot of people who leave without leaving a tip for the servers.

Houlihan's is a higher-end restaurant. Most of the folks I see in their presence as if they have a lot of money. Every now and then a group will walk in and order a hundred-dollar tab exciting the server for a good tip, then they leave the place hurrying out, leaving a measly two-dollar tip on the table. I don't see how folks can do this to people. I understand if the server was terrible, but they must realize the restaurant industry is a very busy place and a stressful job. The servers deserve something no matter what because the timing isn't always on them there are a lot of different factors that go into getting someone their meal. So, think before you walk out of a restaurant leaving little or no tip, if the server waited on you for an hour, they only made a measly two fifty or so without a tip. People should understand this. If you have a little extra, be sure to give it.

23

AUGUST 27

Well, I called the machine shop that has my old fifty-three Buicks engine. I have twelve days left at the center, they told me that they would have my engine ready for me by the time that I leave. I thought it was going to cost around two hundred and fifty dollars they informed me know that the price was double, right at five hundred dollars. I argued with the man a little over the price, but I decided that it wasn't worth the energy of fighting, but I was going to try and talk them down when I went to pick it up. I told him that I would like to pick it up after the seventh of September since that was my release date. He said they would warrant the cylinder that they fixed, so that made me feel comfortable with the work done. I should have around a thousand dollars by the time that I leave. So, plenty to do the work. I also needed to put an engine in my van, so I have a couple of weeks of engine work ahead of me once I'm free.

I got up today, hitting the snooze a half dozen times before climbing out of bed barely moving, feeling rather beat from the last few days of work. Waking up at five in the morning, this routine was starting to wear on me since I have never really worked a real job in my life. I was too used to doing whatever the hell I pleased. I caught the bus this morning bumming a few smokes of a man who looks very similar to Jeff Bridges' character, the dude. I call the man the dude, never really caring to learn his real name. To me, he was just the dude. I would probably never remember his real name anyway because the first thing to pop to mind when I saw the man was the dude. I went to Starbucks to get coffee. I'm starting to become a regular up here since I come in every morning. As I walked in I was greeted with a smile. I was paying for my coffee when I noticed a figurine on the counter made from car parts. The head of the thing was a piston and it had wrenches for arms. For some reason, they had the thing dressed up as a Star Wars character with a robe and a lightsaber. I took the sight of the thing with good faith since I had just talked to the engine shop the day before. Good vibes from the engine character, "WELL GOOD DEAL, I THOUGHT" I'm ready to get back to my projects; I desperately need a wrench in my hand again to turn my brain back on. I have recently been having the sound of my motorcycle engine in my head and as soon as I'm out, I'm going to take the thing out for a good long spin. Maybe taking Megan for a ride if I can convince her to get on the thing with me. Maybe take a good hundred-mile trip or so to break the cobwebs out of the thing and myself for that matter. The jail has been taking a toll on my beat-up body, not enough joint movement for my worn-out bones.

August 30

At work today, they tried to make me wear a hat while washing dishes. I find this to be complete bullshit. I have worked here for weeks now and just now, they say I need to wear a hat "WHAT THE FUCK" I think one of the managers is out to get me for some reason. I guess my hair is getting too long or something looking too much like a hippie these days I guess, "FUCK IT" I really don't care what these bastards think I'm going to see if I can get away with not wearing a hat. Washing dishes, you don't need a goddamn hat. The dishes go through about three different sets of hands before there is any food placed on them at all. Also, it makes me feel like I just joined the tee-ball team. I have never been much of a hat guy anyway. I look terrible with the thing on, I did find though, if I turned it around backwards, I could pull it off. It's not like my hair is falling out or anything, I'm not looking that bad yet. I did receive some good news today though. I might finally be getting out of this goddamn dish room very soon. They are talking about making me a bar back. So, I might very well be making more money in the future. "GOD, I HOPE SO" this working for peanuts is really starting to get to me. I was talking to a server today asking how much she makes, and she told me that she could make around a thousand dollars a week "FUCK YEAH" I thought. That's what I need to get into or preferably be a bartender. I want to work with people. The damn dish room is kind of an anti-social place to work. I prefer working for the people for their stories. You can learn a lot from some people. I also thought that it could be a good time to pick up some more side work for my business. I might have to start carrying around my business cards with me.

Today in the dish room, I was damn near my breaking point. I managed to maintain, but it was starting to feel like the goddamn circus in there. I felt like I was on one of the games where you're strapped to a spinning wheel looking like Leonardo Da Vinci's drawing of man, spinning around and around while the servers throw jagged broken plates and glasses at me, trying to cut me to bits. Luckily the bastards didn't know how to lead well, so I managed to dodge most of the blows. To top it all off, it was a prep day and even the dishwasher had to do some prep and there was hardly any time for me to do anything other than dishes. The only way to explain the situation is that it's pure hell for eight hours straight, it's terrible. I really feel like the jail and my work are trying to break me; the shit gets tough, you know, "REAL LIFE" to top it all off, I had to clean the walls in the dish room as well using bleach. I had managed to get the shit all over my black shirt and pants. One of the servers also managed to get some on her shirt, leaning against the wall as she talked to me. I felt bad about it, but I teased her a little telling her if she wasn't so lazy and leaning on the wall, she wouldn't have messed her shirt up. She laughed; it was at that point that I realized how beautiful Cassidy really was. I don't know how I missed that for so long. During our conversation, we maintained eye contact for a very long time and I had to snap myself out of it, I was getting lost in her soul. After ruining Cassidy's and my shirt and looking like we both had tie-dye on all day. I had to buy a new shirt. I thought about offering Cassidy a new shirt too, but she didn't seem to care.

Later that night, I got back to the jail. I had signed up for the Walmart run the night before, so I was in luck with getting myself some new shirts. This was supposed to be a routine trip to Walmart, "SOON TO PROVE ITSELF OTHERWISE." As we left the jail, there was a newly hired guard driving the van. She told us that she had never driven a vehicle that big before, which was funny because this woman was only about four feet tall. One of the fellows made a joke that he saw her bringing phone books to the van so that she could see over the dash. I looked for the phone books when I got in the van but didn't see any, but the thought of the ordeal was rather entertaining. She was asking us for directions and we managed to get her to Walmart. The whole way though, she was riding the breaks and just barely going the speed limit. She wore rather large lenses in her glasses which I think she might have needed to get her eyes rechecked because she was having a rather tough time seeing the large Walmart sign. Hell, the thing must have been fifty feet tall. I don't know how she missed it. She eventually got us there though, despite the few hiccups. Once we got there, I managed to find everything I needed. I then went to the fruit section buying a kiwi and a peach. For some reason, the other inmates looked at me funny when I got the fruit, but I told them that we had been neglected true sustenance for so long that you must be stupid not to eat some real food every now and again. I always try to replenish when I can. They don't even know the sustenance the body needs anymore, they have been neglected for too long to use to the "SOYLENT GREEN" I paid for my groceries and walked outside, still having about thirty minutes left of our trip before they were picking us back up.

I sat out front eating my fruit as some of my fellow inmates showed up. We sat in a group on bags of potting soil and on a rack where they had potted flowers. One guy bought a carton of cigarettes, being very generous with them, handing some out to everyone. He asked me if I wanted one and I turned down his offer. As we sat, a group of young kids came out of the store, causing a big ruckus, being very loud as they left the building. Harassing the cart boy as they walked past him, "BUNCH OF PRICKS" I thought. They jumped into a large Chevy diesel truck that I'm sure their daddy had bought for them. They saw the group of us sitting out front. They tried to smoke us out with the exhaust of their obnoxious truck, but they had hit the gas too late to hit us, but they did manage to smoke the front door of the place the dumb kids had damn near broken the tires free on the thing as they sped away. They were probably hitting around thirty or forty-five by the time that they flew past the entrance. I thought how offal it would be if they hit some innocent bystander. Then right as they went by, a man and his son came walking out. If they had been thirty seconds earlier, they would have been right in the path of the punks and probably been run down. They had made quite the show in the parking lot. Someone had told the managers that there was a group of kids causing a ruckus. Of course, with my luck, the manager came out and began asking us why we were causing trouble, we then informed them about the group of kids that had just screeched out of the parking lot in their truck. She apologized for falsely accusing us and she went back inside.

About ten minutes later, another man claiming to be a manager walked up on us from the parking lot. He was complaining about us loitering in front of the store. One of the people in our group was sitting in a shopping cart. We had told the man that we had already talked to one of the managers about being out front and telling him that we were not the ones causing a ruckus. He then directed his glance towards the kid in the shopping cart and asked if she told us that it was ok to sit in the shopping carts. The man said we were good to hang out, but he seemed like everything was most certainly not ok. He walked off. About two minutes had passed when suddenly, the man came back with all the Walmart dummies. This time he wanted us to leave at once. One of the kids in the group began telling them that we would be considered a wall if we left the property, not really explaining to the man our situation very well. I could sense the tensions rising between the two of them, I then began talking to a different employee about our situation. I took a different approach as I spoke to him, talking soft and calmly like I had many times before in my life dealing with cops and other so-called authority figures, most of the time talking my way out of the situation with no consequences at all. You must realize I was dealing with a bunch of jailhouse criminals who had never heard of this concept. To make it all worse, the Walmart dummies were getting worked up as well. There was soon to be a great argument. I kept talking to the man patiently, but suddenly, a dumb kid from jail called one of them a "DUMB FUCK" you are fucking idiot man, I had these dummies and you fucked it all up with that one comment, the man that I was talking too then told me that he was calling the cops. God, I wish how ignorant people wouldn't sometimes speak, really. The punk was just making a fool of himself, but the jail dummies were egging the kid on. At this point, it turned into a savage battle between the apes, the dumb asses from jail, screeching and throwing shit and the Walmart employees doing the same, it was a useless exertion of energy. Luckily a few other inmates and I were not performing in this manner, we were smarter than that, we had far surpassed the Stone Age and learned how to cope in a civil matter. I was still talking to the manager as he was on the phone with the cops. I was giving him the information about the jail, so he could relay the information to the police. He seemed relieved that there was someone who wasn't a complete dumbass around. I began staring at the dumb kid yelling profanities at the employees. I felt like walking over and slapping the ignorant fucker. I managed to hold back; I felt like the old man of the group, being the only one mature enough to have a normal conversation without acting a fool.

At this point, the young guard had shown up. She looked as if she was about to have a complete mental breakdown. This was her first trip driving us around and she had to deal with this kind of shit. I felt sorry for her. She could barely speak, so I then had to speak for her.

We resolved the situation and walked back to the van that was parked at the back of the lot. We got about half way there when a cop car went past me; I gave them the peace sign as he went by. Another cop in the lane over sped towards the front of the store. I knew I would soon be talking to these officers. We got to the bus and everyone loaded in except for me being the last. The guard was looking at me funny because I wasn't getting in the van; I was looking back at the entrance to Walmart, watching the two cops walking towards the van. When the guard told me to get in, I pointed towards the police officers walking our way. I started walking towards them; I told the first cop that he couldn't do much to us because we were already in jail. "HE CHUCKLED A LITTLE" I then told them what had gone on, he seemed like a cool cop till he asked about the kid who was mouthing off. His demeanor completely changed as he talked to the punk in the van. One good thing about the kid I'll give him is that he said if there was to be trouble about what he said to the Walmart employee he would take the blame in full. I gave him some credit for that, but if the idiot had just kept his mouth shut in the first place, we wouldn't be in this mess at all. As the cop called him out for being a punk, he began again talking his shit. I pictured the cop removing the kid from the bus and swatting his ass with a paddle over his knee because that's what the kid needed.

It was funny and tragic to watch because it seemed like the cop himself liked to escalate the kid. They were both feeding off each other's amped-up attitudes. I looked at the cop with a look of disgust as they gave the kid a sense of power by arguing with him. At that point, I couldn't decide who was wrong, I looked at the cop, signaling him to just drop the whole thing and let us go and he did. "THANK GOD" I thought. The police shut the door and we left; I then wondered if any of us were going to get into any trouble because of the whole ordeal. We pulled out of the parking lot, now running late. The jail called the guard asking if everything was ok because of the tardiness, she informed them that we had a slight incident and that she would elaborate on the situation when we arrived back at the jail. One of the police that was at Walmart was following us on our trip back, I think to try and make the kid who was arguing nervous about what he did. Suddenly right before we were about to make the turn, the cop sped past the bus. The tension was now lifted even the driver finally relaxed. Then out of nowhere, the radio came to life once more, saying that the sheriff's office had called saying that the lady was driving without her headlights on. She panicked once more and checked the lights, but they were on, so again she was confused. She radioed back, saying that they were, in fact, on. We pulled back into the jail parking lot and everyone thought that we were going to be searched very thoroughly. I had bought my shirts and had put one under my top shirt. I then told the guard I did so that I would not get into trouble when they searched us all while we were getting patted in. Suddenly, they informed us that none of us could leave the intake room. We had to wait for some reason. A few of us decided that we were not going to Walmart again because of the inconvenience. "HELL" I thought after that ordeal, no one was going to be able to go anymore. "THEY FUCKED IT UP" I personally didnn't have to worry, though, because I would have left in a week anyway, so I have no worries if they decided to revoke the trips for pure ignorance. Not my problem at all. We sat around waiting to be talked to by some higher authority figure, but they never came, so they let us go after about fifteen minutes. I hurried to get to bed because now the ordeal was the talk of the place. Just a bunch of baboons getting excited over a stupid ordeal, if you're going to tell stories, at least tell some good ones.

It was the following day after the whole Walmart ordeal. I woke up right at eleven getting up and hurrying down to the property office to get the shirts that I had bought the day before. The door to the place was shut, so I asked the main desk when they would be open, she said they had opened from ten to eleven. As I was talking to the main desk clerk, a fellow inmate knocked on the door of the property office. The property office lady opened it five minutes late. She preceded to hand the man's stuff to him. I just stood behind the man in line, waiting for them to finish up. Once they did, I stepped up to the window to ask for my shirts, the lady immediately began to change and warp into a nasty figure, demanding that I tell her the time. I told her that it was eleven of five. She then barked at me, demanding me to tell her why I wasn't there at the allotted time. Really, I had no clue what time that was, especially because the lady had just handed the other guy his stuff when he too was late. She barked that I had come too late, I watched as the woman became enraged with anger, she had a short fuse. The worst part of the thing is I could see my bag of things sitting on the table right in front of her. All she had to do was hand the bag to me. She wouldn't even have to take a step. Her mouth was foaming with rage now, snarling and showing her fierce bite. I thought to reach in and grab my bag and make a run for it, but she was ready to pounce like a dog trying to reach the mailman. "PURE FURY AND HATE" with no real reason why. The woman barked at me again, telling me that they were going to be open again at seven that night, I told her that I needed my shirts before seven, this was a lie, but she didn't know any different. It was only a partial lie because of the bleach that I had spilled on my shirt. Really though, I didn't work for a couple of days. I had to try very hard not to talk back to the woman for being a complete bitch as she snapped her teeth at me and foamed from the mouth. I really should have rolled up a newspaper and swatted her ass with it and said, "BAD DOG" I walked away slowly, making sure not to break eye contact with the beast, getting about fifteen feet away, then making a desperate dash for the door. I was thinking to myself on my way back to my room about the haunting that these guards will receive later in life. Only the ones that are pricks, but I hope they receive the hatred they have given back before they die. Really when it comes down to it, they are the true beasts, the ones that need to be put on a leash and locked in cages. I can understand using force in certain situations when there is no mutual respect. A lot of these guards and police walk around like ticking time bombs, waiting for the perfect moment to blow. To me, this is funny as hell because they really are no better than us all, but the badge makes them entitled to explode. The cops yesterday were the perfect example of this. They had already been told the kid was talking back by the time they had gotten over to him and they proceeded to sit to argue with the kid for ten minutes, just feeding each other's fire. This sickens me that there are no real adults anymore, just children everywhere and worst of all, the police force is full of them. It's becoming a dangerous thing anymore, children teaching children neither of which really knowing the right way. The biggest problem I see right now is the elders are being pushed aside now because of technology. No time to sit and eat as a family anymore or even say hi to each other when we walk in the door, these are crucial moments to get to know your children and teach them. With the elders running out of time and the future not wanting to learn basic principles, we in fact have kids teaching kids. It's funny how the world works, nothing good comes fast. I like to compare it to my grandmas' biscuits and gravy, both being handmade, I don't care if it was my grandma's worst day, her biscuits and gravy would taste better than any store-bought or restaurant. The reason being is that she has spent years perfecting her recipe, it took time. I do know every now and again, you can get lucky and get something great in a short time, but it is rare. My cars and boats are the same way. I have nice and unique things because I found them and put the time in to make them nice again.

I feel like, as a society, we are trying to grow too fast, leaving out important processes along the way. No one listens to the old-timers anymore, they just put them in a home or a hole to rot away, never bringing the kids by to get to learn from them. The old wisdom being lost and pushed aside, fine cars, buildings and furniture being pushed aside and forgotten, leaving us all in a time of garbage and confusion, the soul of mankind being sucked out of each one of us. With the rubbish, we watch on TV and each time we ride in our plastic cars and go to our prefabricated buildings for work. Being unique is going away. Any more you can go to almost any town and the place is a replica of the last one down the road. "THE KIDS WILL RUIN IT ALL, BUT I'M JUST GUNNA SIT BACK AND WATCH THE WHOLE SHITHOUSE GO UP IN FLAMES".

Made in the USA
Monee, IL
16 October 2023